Workbook
SCOPE 1

Lewis Lansford

Ben Wetz

OXFORD
UNIVERSITY PRESS

Contents

A Starter

VOCABULARY

School

1 ✪ **Match the questions and answers.**

1 Who is our physics teacher? ___d___
2 Where's the school canteen? ....
3 What time is the French class? ....
4 When's the next school sports day? ....
5 Is PE in the gym today? ....
6 How old is this computer? ....

a It's at 10 o'clock.
b No, it's on the field.
c It's in May.
d Mr Morgan.
e About ten years old.
f It's on the first floor.

2 ✪✪ **Complete the text with the words below.**

biology	~~communication~~	easy
exam	good	gym	lab	PE

I like school. ICT (information and ¹ _communication_ technology) is my favourite subject. It's in the computer ² .... every morning at 9 o'clock. I also like ³ .... (physical education). I'm ⁴ .... at sport. It's in the ⁵ .... or on the field at 10 o'clock. I'm not very good at chemistry or ⁶ .... – science is difficult. My maths ⁷ .... is today, but that's OK. It's ⁸ .... I'm brilliant at maths.

3 ✪✪✪ **Answer the questions.**

1 What's your favourite subject?
....

2 Who's your English teacher?
....

3 What are you good at?
....

4 When's your next exam?
....

GRAMMAR

Present simple of *be*: questions and short answers

4 ✪✪ **Complete each sentence with the correct form of the verb *to be*.**

1 _Are_ you good at sport?
2 .... English your favourite subject?
3 .... football matches interesting?
4 .... your teachers friendly?
5 .... your town quiet?
6 .... your classrooms modern?
7 .... TV boring?

5 ✪✪✪ **Answer the questions in exercise 4 above.**

1 ....
2 ....
3 ....
4 ....
5 ....
6 ....
7 ....

Demonstrative pronouns

6 ✪✪ **Complete the conversation with *this*, *that*, *these* or *those*.**

Tom Who are ¹ _those_ people over there?
Dan ² .... man is my dad and ³ .... two boys over there are my brothers.
Mum Hello, Dan.
Dan Hi, Mum. ⁴ .... is my friend, Tom.
Mum Nice to meet you, Tom. Dan, I found ⁵ .... keys outside. Are they yours?
Dan No, ⁶ .... aren't my keys.
Tom Oh, they're mine!

7 ✪✪✪ **Write four sentences about things around you. Use *this*, *that*, *these* and *those*.**

Those are my brother's pencils
1 ....
2 ....
3 ....
4 ....

B Starter

Describing people

1 ✪ **Choose the correct words.**

1 Cathy is **quite** / **average** height.
2 Our teacher's got a **beard** / **hair**.
3 My mum's got **slim** / **wavy** hair.
4 Abdullah and Samira have got **straight** / **brown** eyes.
5 Ed's **medium-length** / **quite** tall.
6 My dad hasn't got any **hair** / **bald**.
7 Amber's got **long** / **green** eyes.
8 Ann's hair is **blond** / **tall**.

2 ✪✪ **Complete the text with the words below.**

bald	blue	curly	dark	heavy
long	moustache	short	~~tall~~	

My name's Lisa and I'm 16 years old. I'm quite **¹** tall and I'm average build. I've got **²** .... eyes. My hair is blond, straight and **³** ....
My sister, Sue, is ten. She isn't tall – she's quite **⁴** .... Her hair isn't blond and straight, it's **⁵** .... and **⁶** .... She isn't **⁷** .... – she's quite slim. Our dad's name is Jack. He's average height and he's got a **⁸** .... He doesn't have any hair – he's **⁹** .... !

3 ✪✪✪ **Write five sentences describing yourself, your friends and your family.**

1 My dad's bald.
2 ....
3 ....
4 ....
5 ....

Order of adjectives

4 ✪✪ **Rewrite the sentences using the word(s) in brackets.**

1 Lisa's got brown hair. (curly / long)
   Lisa's got long, curly, brown hair.
2 He's slim. (tall / and)
   ....
3 I've got short hair. (dark)
   ....
4 Cathy is average height. (average build / and)
   ....
5 My dad's got a moustache. (grey / long)
   ....

5 ✪✪✪ **Write a description of Adam.**

1.6 m →

Adam

have got

6 ✪✪ **Correct the mistakes in bold.**

A **¹Haven't** your school got a library?   Has
B Yes, it **²haven't**.   ....
A **³Has** your classmates got mobile phones?   ....
B No, they **⁴have**.   ....
A **⁵Have** your English teacher got a beard?   ....
B No, he **⁶has**.   ....

7 ✪✪✪ **Complete the conversation with the correct form of *have* or *have got*.**

A **¹** Have you got any brothers or sisters?
B I **²** .... two brothers. Their names are Ed and Jack. Ed **³** .... a beard, but Jack **⁴** ....
A **⁵** .... they .... brown hair like you?
B No, they **⁶** .... blond hair. They **⁷** .... brown hair.

C Starter

VOCABULARY

At home

1 ⭐ Match the words below with the things in the picture.

> armchair bed bookcase chair chest of drawers
> desk lamp mirror ~~picture~~ wardrobe

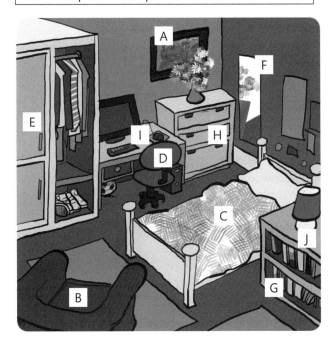

A ..picture......

B ....

C ....

D ....

E ....

Г ....

G ....

H ....

I ....

J ....

Prepositions of place

2 ⭐⭐ Complete the sentences about the picture in exercise 1. Use the prepositions below.

> ~~above~~ behind near in
> in front of next to on under

1 The picture ..is above the.. chest of drawers.

2 The clothes .... the wardrobe.

3 The chair .... the desk.

4 The football .... the desk.

5 The picture .... the flowers.

6 The lamp .... the bookcase.

7 The armchair is .... the bed.

8 The desk .... the wardrobe.

GRAMMAR

a, an, some and any

3 ⭐⭐ Complete the conversation with *a, an, some* or *any*.

A Have you got [1] ..any.. pictures in your new house?

B Yes, I've got [2] .... picture in the living room.

A Have you got [3] .... armchair?

B No, but we've got [4] .... sofa.

A I've got [5] .... chairs I don't want. Would you like them?

B Great! I haven't got [6] .... chairs in the kitchen.

4 ⭐⭐⭐ Write about your bedroom or a room in your house using *a, an, some* and *any*. Use the model text to help.

> I haven't got any pictures in my room. I've got some books, but I haven't got a bookcase, so my books are on an armchair. I haven't got a computer, but I've got some pens and paper for writing.

....

....

....

....

there is, there are

5 ⭐⭐ Complete the text with *there's, there isn't, there are* or *there aren't*.

> **My school**
> My name's Adam and I'm at Priory School in Manchester. Priory is a small school – [1] ..there are.. only 200 students here. It's a school for boys, so [2] .... any girls. [3] .... 20 or 30 teachers and they teach a lot of different subjects. I like sport. [4] .... a big gym for our PE classes – that's important for me! [5] .... also two excellent PE teachers. However, [6] .... a swimming pool here at Priory School – we go to the city centre for swimming classes.

6 ⭐⭐⭐ Write four sentences about your school. Use *there's, there isn't, there are* and *there aren't*.

1 ....

2 ....

3 ....

4 ....

Hi Erin!

A I'm in the Canadian city of Montreal with my mum and dad and my sister, Sarah. It's a fantastic city with a ¹ population of about 1.6 million. We're here for one month with my mum's sister at her house.

B Liz, my mum's sister, ² .... comes from London. She loves Montreal and she says it's her home now. Her husband is Canadian, and her children are Canadian, too.

C Montreal is a very interesting place! Most people speak both English and French. At least 56% of the people speak French at home. They generally speak to me in French in the shops and cafés, but when I don't understand, they speak in perfect English. So the two languages ³ .... well, and everyone is very friendly and helpful.

D Mum speaks good French and she practises every day, but sometimes she doesn't understand the Canadian French pronunciation. Sarah also speaks French with the local people. She studies French at school.

E Montreal is very ⁴ .... There are people from many different ⁵ .... and countries. There are lots of different types of food here. Sometimes we have lunch in an Italian ⁶ .... on Saint Laurent Boulevard in the 'Little Italy' part of the city. Some people speak Italian there! On other days we eat at the Chinese restaurants in the 'Chinatown' area. That's my favourite food!

Best wishes,

Emma

1 ✪ **Complete the email with six of the words below.**

| cosmopolitan cultures deli mix |
| originally ~~population~~ race reputation |

2 ✪ **Read the email again. Match the headings 1–5 with the paragraphs A–E.**

1 Places to eat   E
2 Where I am   ......
3 Different languages   ......
4 My mum's sister   ......
5 My mum and my sister   ......

3 ✪✪ **Correct the mistakes in bold.**

1 Emma is in Montreal, in **France**.
   Canada
2 1.6 million **families** live in Montreal.
   ....
3 Liz is originally from **Canada**. ....
4 Most people in Montreal speak **Canadian** and French. ....
5 Sarah studies **English** at school. ....
6 Emma eats in **French** delis and Chinese restaurants. ....

4 ✪✪ **Complete the sentences with the words below.**

| ~~Canada~~ Canadian Chinese |
| English French Italian |

1 Liz's husband is from Canada .
2 Generally people in Montreal speak .... as well as French.
3 Most people speak in .... at home.
4 Emma's mum has some problems understanding .... French.
5 On Saint Laurent Boulevard, you can hear some people speaking ....
6 Emma's favourite food is .... food.

5 ✪✪✪ **Answer the questions.**

1 Would you like to visit Montreal? Why / Why not?
   ....
2 What languages do people in your city or country speak?
   ....
3 What kinds of food do you like (e.g. Italian, Chinese)?
   ....

Vocabulary

Countries and nationalities

1 ✪ **Match the sentence halves.**

1 China's capital city is _d_
2 London's climate is ......
3 Canada's currency is ......
4 Saudi Arabia's main export is ......
5 The nationality of people from Poland is ......
6 Brazil's national sport is ......
7 Canada has two official languages.
   They are English and ......
8 Turkey's population is ......

a French.
b Polish.
c the Canadian dollar.
d Beijing.
e about 75 million.
f football.
g oil.
h cold and wet.

2 ✪✪ **Complete the text with words from exercise 1.**

I'm from Malta, which means my **¹** _nationality_ is Maltese. Malta is an island in the Mediterranean Sea. The **²** .... of the country is about 400,000. I live in the **³** .... , which is called Valletta. It's a small city, with about 6000 people, and it's very old. We have two **⁴** .... in my country: Maltese and English. Everyone speaks both Maltese and English. Malta's **⁵** .... is football. Every town and city has a team. I support my city's team – Valletta Football Club. Malta's **⁶** .... is very nice. It's a bit cool and rainy in the winter, but warm or hot in the summer. Our **⁷** .... is the euro (€), the same as France, Germany and other European countries. **⁸** .... from Malta include medicines, books and toys.

3 ✪✪ **Complete the chart.**

England	→	**¹** English
²	→	French
Germany	→	**³**
⁴	→	Indian
Lebanon	→	**⁵**
⁶	→	Polish
Spain	→	**⁷**
⁸	→	Turkish
Yemen	→	**⁹**

4 ✪✪ **Choose the correct words.**

1 About 10% of the **Egypt / Egypt's /** ⟨**Egyptian**⟩ population lives in Cairo.
2 Spain's **national sport / climate / currency** is hot in the summer.
3 **Italy / Italy's / Italian** capital city is Rome.
4 TVs and computers are important **China / China's / Chinese** exports.
5 The official language of France is **Paris / the euro / French**.
6 The nationality of a person from London is **England / English / football**.

5 ✪✪✪ **Write four sentences about your home country. Use four or more of the words below.**

capital city   climate   currency   export   nationality
national sport   official languages   population

   The capital city of England is London.
1 ....
2 ....
3 ....
4 ....

Present simple: positive and negative

1 ✪ **Choose the correct words.**

1 We (come) / comes from Germany.
2 This bookshop **have** / **has** Polish books.
3 You **don't** / **doesn't** study French every day.
4 I **watch** / **watches** Arabic TV every weekend.
5 He doesn't **understand** / **understands** Turkish.
6 Peter **eat** / **eats** Chinese food every Friday.
7 They **live** / **lives** in Madrid, Spain's capital city.
8 Mrs Brown **don't** / **doesn't** like American music.

2 ✪✪ **Complete the text with the correct form of the verbs in brackets.**

Hi! My name's Yasmin. I'm 15 and I'm from Casablanca in Morocco. I ¹ _speak_ (speak) three languages – Arabic, French and English. At home, we always ² .... (use) Arabic or French.

My parents ³ .... (not speak) English. There are six people in my family – me, my mum, my dad and my three brothers. I ⁴ .... (go) to an international school and we ⁵ .... (use) French in class. We also ⁶ .... (study) English for four or five hours a week. My teacher, Monsieur Joubert, ⁷ .... (come) from France. He ⁸ .... (be) a really good teacher. He ⁹ .... (speak) six languages, but he ¹⁰ .... (not speak) very good Arabic! Sometimes my best friend, Asma, ¹¹ .... (use) Arabic in class, but Monsieur Joubert ¹² .... (not understand)!

3 ✪✪ **Rewrite the positive sentences in the negative form and the negative sentences in the positive form.**

1 Fahad likes football.
  Fahad doesn't like football.
2 Mike studies science at university.
  ....
3 Max doesn't speak Portuguese.
  ....
4 My sister finishes school at 3 o'clock.
  ....
5 Our teacher doesn't understand Arabic.
  ....
6 My mum and dad work in a shop.
  ....

4 ✪✪✪ **Look at the chart. What do Rob and Marian do after school? Write four more positive and four more negative sentences.**

	Rob	Marian
read books at home	✓	✗
study French at a language school	✗	✓
play football with friends	✓	✗
go to music lessons	✗	✓
chat on the internet with friends	✓	✓
watch TV at home	✗	✗

Positive
1 Rob _reads books at home._
2 Marian ....
3 Rob ....
4 Marian ....
5 Rob and Marian ....

Negative
6 Marian _doesn't read books at home._
7 Rob ....
8 Marian ....
9 Rob ....
10 Rob and Marian ....

5 ✪✪✪ **Write two positive and two negative sentences about what you do and don't do after school.**

I play football.
1 ....
2 ....

I don't study Arabic.
3 ....
4 ....

Daily routines

1 ✪ Complete the daily routines with the words below.

do fetch go have have out say school the animals up

1 wake _up_ ....
2 .... a break
3 .... exercise
4 .... dinner
5 .... your prayers

6 feed ....
7 .... to sleep
8 hang ....
9 .... water
10 finish ....

2 ✪✪ Match the phrases 1–10 in exercise 1 with the pictures A–J.

A 1   B   C   D   E

F   G   H   I   J

3 ✪✪ Look at the chart. Then complete the sentences with the words below.

always never often sometimes usually

1 Jane _never_ gets up at 8.00.

2 She .... gets up at 7.00.

3 She .... has breakfast at 7.30.

4 She .... has breakfast at 7.15.

5 She .... goes to bed at 10.30.

Jane's week	get up at 7.00	breakfast at 7.15	breakfast at 7.30	go to bed at 10.30
Monday	✓	✓		✓
Tuesday	✓		✓	
Wednesday	✓		✓	✓
Thursday	✓		✓	
Friday	✓		✓	✓
Saturday	✓	✓		
Sunday	✓		✓	✓

4 ✪✪✪ Write six sentences about your day.

I always go to school at 8 o'clock.

1 ....
2 ....
3 ....
4 ....
5 ....
6 ....

Present simple: questions

1 ✪ **Choose the correct words.**

1 **When** / What do you play tennis?
2 Who **do** / **does** he hang out with after school?
3 Where do they **live** / **lives**?
4 **Do** / **Does** she study French?
5 **What** / **How** time do they get up?
6 Do you **study** / **studies** at the weekend?
7 **When** / **How** often do you play football?
8 **Who** / **Where** does your sister live?

2 ✪✪ **Match the answers a–h with the questions 1–8 in exercise 1.**

a No, she studies Spanish.   4
b They live in London.   ....
c With his friend Aziz.   ....
d Yes, I do. I usually study English.   ....
e At 10 o'clock on Sundays.   ....
f They usually get up at 6 o'clock.   ....
g She lives in Oman.   ....
h I play every weekend.   ....

3 ✪✪ **Complete the conversation with the words below.**

> Do Does speak speaks What
> ~~What's~~ When Where Who

Aziz   ¹ _What's_ your name?
Fahad My name's Fahad.
Aziz   ² .... do you live?
Fahad I live in Manchester, in the UK.
Aziz   ³ .... do you live with?
Fahad With my parents and my sister.
Aziz   ⁴ .... languages do you speak?
Fahad I ⁵ .... Arabic and English.
Aziz   ⁶ .... you study English?
Fahad Yes, I study English at school.
Aziz   ⁷ .... your sister speak English?
Fahad Yes, she does. She ⁸ .... English and Arabic.
Aziz   ⁹ .... do you do your homework?
Fahad Every night!

4 ✪✪ **Correct the mistakes in bold.**

1 A How often does Dave ~~plays~~ football?
     play
  B Every day!
2 A **Where** does Asma hang out with at the weekend? ....
  B Her friends, Jenna and Yasmin.
3 A **Do** Ed speak Spanish? ....
  B Yes.
4 A Do Lisa and Jane study French?
  B Yes, they **does**. ....
5 A **When** does Nasir do before school?
     ....
  B He does exercise.
6 A **Who** often does Karen watch TV? ....
  B Only at the weekends.
7 A Do you live in Jordan?
  B Yes, I **live**. ....

5 ✪✪✪ **Complete the sentences about yourself. Then write a question for each sentence.**

1 A _When do you usually study?_
  You I usually study _after school._
2 A .... ?
  You I do exercise ....
3 A .... ?
  You I hang out with ....
4 A .... ?
  You In the evenings, I often ....
5 A .... ?
  You I like going to ....

6 ✪✪✪ **Write a conversation between yourself and a friend. Ask your friend about their routines and habits.**

A ....
B ....
A ....
B ....
A ....
B ....

A country factfile

LANGUAGE FOCUS *also*

1 ✪ Write *also* in the correct position in each sentence.

1 People speak English in Canada. They ..also.. speak .... French in some cities.
2 Andy is very clever. He .... is .... very friendly.
3 Tom plays the piano. He .... plays .... the guitar.
4 We study English at school and we .... study .... French or German.
5 There are some Italian delis and there .... are .... some Chinese restaurants on this street.
6 My dad is a teacher and my mother .... is .... a teacher.

2 ✪✪ Complete the sentences. Use your imagination!
Use *also* in your sentences.

1 Cathy is interested in history. She ....
2 Bill plays the piano. He ....
3 Sam is good at maths. He ....
4 In the evenings, I watch TV. I ....
5 There is a park near my house. There ....
6 Adam likes football. He ....

TASK Factfile

3 ✪✪ Read the factfile about England and complete the form.

Country and language factfile: England

England is in north-west Europe and is the largest country in the UK. (The UK also includes Scotland, Wales and Northern Ireland.) The population of England is about 53 million. The capital city is London and other major cities include Birmingham, Leeds, Sheffield and Manchester. The currency is the pound sterling. England is only 34 km from France and is linked by a tunnel under the English Channel.

Outside the metropolitan areas, England is mostly agricultural land, hills and mountains. The climate is temperate with mild winters and warm summers.

English is the official language of England. England is a cosmopolitan, multicultural country with a lot of immigration, particularly from the Indian sub-continent. Other languages spoken in England include Punjabi, Urdu, Bengali and Polish.

The national sport of England is football. Other popular sports include rugby and cricket.

England is famous for many things, including its royal family, London landmarks such as Big Ben, and the writer William Shakespeare.

England

Bordering countries: Forms the UK with [1] Wales , [2] .... and Northern Ireland. Nearest other countries are Ireland and [3] ....

Population: [4] ....

Capital city: [5] ....

Other major cities: Birmingham, [6] .... , Sheffield, [7] ....

Landscape: agricultural land, [8] .... and [9] ....

Climate: temperate with [10] .... summers and [11] .... winters

Official language: [12] ....

Other languages: Punjabi, [13] .... , Bengali, [14] ....

Sports: [15] .... , [16] .... and cricket

Famous for: [17] .... , London landmarks such as Big Ben, and [18] ....

4 ✪✪✪ Write a factfile about another country. Use the factfile from exercise 3 as a model.

- Choose a country to write about.
- Use books or the internet to research the country and its language(s).
- Write 100–150 words.

Review Unit 1 in the Student's Book and complete the exercises below. Think about your progress and choose one of the faces.

READING — The world in one city

1 Read the text on page 11 of the Student's Book again. Answer the questions.

1 Give two facts about the people of London.

- _____
- _____

2 What do Jacek and Zaida like about London?

_____
_____
_____

I can understand a text about multicultural London.

VOCABULARY

2 Complete the form with the words below. Then answer the question.

| capital city | currency | exports | ~~nationality~~ | population |

Canada

1 _nationality_ : Canadian
2 _____ : 35 million
3 _____ : Ottawa
4 _____ : wood products, oil
5 _____ : Canadian dollar

Write a fact about your home country.

_____

I can talk about countries and nationalities.

3 Complete the sentences. Use four more of the phrases below.

do exercise	feed the animals	fetch water
finish school	~~go to sleep~~	hang out with friends
have a break	have dinner	say prayers	wake up

1 I always _go to sleep_ at _10 o'clock_.
2 I usually _____ on _____.
3 I often _____ at _____.
4 I sometimes _____ in _____.
5 I never _____ on _____.

I can talk about daily routines and use adverbs of frequency.

GRAMMAR

4 Complete the sentences with the present simple form of the verbs in brackets.

1 Amira _lives_ (live) in Cairo.
2 Tom and Kevin _____ (not like) watching TV.
3 Lana _____ (not speak) German.
4 I _____ (study) every day after school.
5 Mr Jones _____ (teach) English.

I can talk about habits and facts.

5 Complete the conversations with the words below.

| do | does | how | ~~speak~~ |

1 A Do you _speak_ French?
  B Yes, I do.
2 A _____ they watch TV after school?
  B No, they don't.
3 A _____ often do you have music lessons?
  B Every day.
4 A _____ Bill know Samir?
  B No, he doesn't.

I can ask about routines and habits.

SPEAKING

6 Correct the mistakes in the phrases in bold.

Jane Hi, Amy. ¹**What are things?**
      How _____

Amy   Good, thanks. ²**This my Jordanian friend,** Aleena. _____

Aleena Hi there!

Jane Hello! Sorry, what's your name?

Aleena Aleena.

Jane ³**How you do spell that?** _____

Aleena It's A-L-E-E-N-A.

Jane Oh, right. ⁴**Nice meet you,** Aleena.
      _____

Aleena And you.

Jane ⁵**Sees you around.** _____

I can introduce people.

1 Read the extract. Number the events in the correct order 1–6.

<u>1</u> Tom starts painting the fence.

.... Joe asks to paint the fence.

.... Joe goes over to Tom and speaks to him.

.... Joe watches Tom paint the fence.

.... Tom gives the brush to Joe and Joe starts painting.

.... Tom tells Joe that he likes painting fences.

2 Read the extract again and choose the correct answers.

1 Where does Tom live?
  a in a village
  b in a town

2 Tom and Joe … .
  a are brothers
  b are friends

3 Joe had plans to … before he met Tom.
  a go to the river
  b paint the fence

4 After watching Tom paint the fence for five minutes, Joe … .
  a becomes interested in painting
  b gets bored

5 Joe … .
  a gives Tom some of his apple
  b gives Tom all of his apple

3 Answer the questions. Look at the text, and use your own words and ideas.

1 Who do you think Tom lives with?

2 Whose fence do you think Tom is painting?

3 What kind of person is Tom? What is his personality?

4 Why is Tom happy at the end of the extract?

4 What do you think happens next? Write a short paragraph (75–100 words). Begin with the line below.

More friends came to laugh at Tom, but soon they all wanted to paint, too. By the afternoon, …

Tom came out of his house with a brush and a big pot of white paint in his hand. He looked at the fence; it was three metres high and 30 metres long. He put his brush in the paint and painted some of the fence. He did it again. Then he stopped and looked at the fence, put down his brush and sat down. There were hours of work in front of him and he was the unhappiest boy in the village.

After ten minutes Tom had an idea, a wonderful idea. He took up the brush again and began work. He saw his friend Joe Harper in the street, but he didn't look at him. Joe had an apple in his hand. He came up to Tom and looked at the fence.

'I *am* sorry, Tom.' Tom said nothing. The paint brush moved up and down.

'Working for your aunt?' said Joe. 'I'm going down to the river. I'm sorry you can't come with me.'

Tom put down his brush. 'You call this work?' he said.

'Painting a fence?' said Joe. 'Of course it's work!'

'Perhaps it is and perhaps it isn't. But I like it,' said Tom. 'I can go to the river any day. I can't paint a fence very often.'

Joe watched Tom for about five minutes. Tom painted very slowly and carefully. He often stopped, moved back from the fence and looked at his work with a smile. Joe began to get very interested, and said:

'Tom, can I paint a little?'

Tom thought for a second. 'I'm sorry, Joe. You see, my aunt wants me to do it because I'm good at painting. My brother Sid wanted to paint, too, but she said no.'

'Oh, please, Tom, just a little. I'm good at painting, too. Hey, do you want some of my apple?'

'No, Joe, I can't–'

'OK, you can have all my apple!'

Tom gave Joe the brush. He did not smile, but for the first time that day he was a very happy boy. He sat down and ate Joe's apple.

Family life

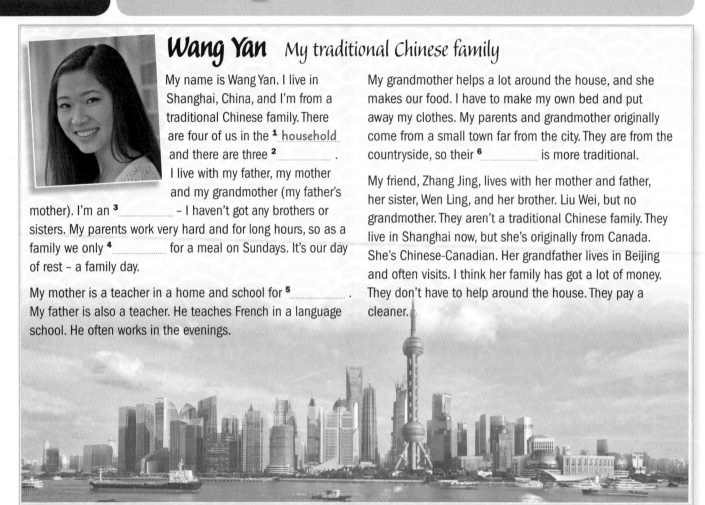

Wang Yan My traditional Chinese family

My name is Wang Yan. I live in Shanghai, China, and I'm from a traditional Chinese family. There are four of us in the **¹** household and there are three **²** _____ . I live with my father, my mother and my grandmother (my father's mother). I'm an **³** _____ – I haven't got any brothers or sisters. My parents work very hard and for long hours, so as a family we only **⁴** _____ for a meal on Sundays. It's our day of rest – a family day.

My mother is a teacher in a home and school for **⁵** _____ . My father is also a teacher. He teaches French in a language school. He often works in the evenings.

My grandmother helps a lot around the house, and she makes our food. I have to make my own bed and put away my clothes. My parents and grandmother originally come from a small town far from the city. They are from the countryside, so their **⁶** _____ is more traditional.

My friend, Zhang Jing, lives with her mother and father, her sister, Wen Ling, and her brother. Liu Wei, but no grandmother. They aren't a traditional Chinese family. They live in Shanghai now, but she's originally from Canada. She's Chinese-Canadian. Her grandfather lives in Beijing and often visits. I think her family has got a lot of money. They don't have to help around the house. They pay a cleaner.

1 ⭐ **Complete the text with six of the words below.**

background	full-time	gather	generations
~~household~~	only child	orphans	siblings

2 ⭐ **Read the text again and complete the sentences with the correct name.**

1 _____ is an only child.
2 _____ has two siblings.
3 _____ is a boy.

3 ⭐⭐ **Read the text again. Write** *true* **or** *false*. **Correct the false sentences.**

1 Wang Yan lives with her daughter and parents. _____
2 Wang Yan hasn't got a brother. _____
3 Wang Yan doesn't have to help around the house. _____
4 Zhang Jing's family isn't traditional. _____
5 Zhang Jing doesn't live with her grandfather. _____
6 Zhang Jing helps a lot around the house. _____

4 ⭐⭐ **Choose the correct answers.**

1 How many people does Wang Yan live with?
   a two   b three   c four
2 How many brothers and sisters has Wang Yan got?
   a none   b one   c two
3 Which job does Wang Yan do at home?
   a makes food   b teaches orphans   c makes her bed
4 Where are Wang Yan's parents from?
   a Shanghai   b another country   c a small town
5 How many people does Zhang Jing live with?
   a three   b four   c five
6 Who does the jobs in Zhang Jing's household?
   a a cleaner   b her mother   c the children

5 ⭐⭐⭐ **Answer the questions.**

1 Who lives in your household?
   _____
2 Who does the household jobs?
   _____
3 Do you have a 'family day' or a time when everyone in the family gathers? What do you do?
   _____

Helping at home

1 ⭐ Complete the list of jobs with the words below.

| bed clothes dinner dishwasher room rubbish |
| ~~shopping bags~~ table vacuuming washing |

JOBS

1 unpack the ¹ shopping bags

2 put away my ² ....

3 make ³ ....

4 do the ⁴ .... -up and load
   the ⁵ ....

5 clear the ⁶ ....

6 do the ⁷ ....

7 take out the ⁸ ....

8 make my ⁹ ....

9 tidy up my ¹⁰ ....

2 ⭐ How often do you do the jobs in exercise 1?
Write each job in the correct place.

I never ...	I sometimes ...
I often ...	**I ... every day.**

3 ⭐⭐ Complete the text with the verbs from exercise 1.

Sharing the work at home

'I always ¹ do the vacuuming on Saturdays,' says
Helen Smith. She's a university student, but she
lives at home with her parents. 'On Fridays, my dad
goes shopping, but I always ² .... the
shopping while Dad ³ .... dinner. After
dinner, Mum and I ⁴ .... the table and
then ⁵ .... the dishwasher. Finally, we
⁶ .... the rubbish.'

Helen's mum and dad work full time in the city so
everybody has busy lives. 'We take the jobs in turns,' says
Helen. 'We like helping each other. On Saturday mornings
we ⁷ .... our rooms, ⁸ ....
our beds and ⁹ .... our clothes. We take it
in turns to ¹⁰ .... the vacuuming. Some of
my friends do the same,' she says.

4 ⭐⭐ Match the verbs 1–6 with the pictures A–F.

1 unplug   B   4 unfold   ....

2 unwrap   ....   5 unlock   ....

3 undo   ....   6 unload   ....

 A    B

 C   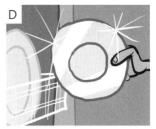 D

 E    F

5 ⭐⭐ Complete the sentences with the verbs from exercise 4.

1 Hello, Yusuf! It's me, Talib! Unlock the front
   door. Let me in!

2 .... that piece of paper and read it.
   It's a note from your father.

3 I can't take off my shoe because I can't
   .... the laces.

4 The plates are clean. Please help me
   .... the dishwasher.

5 There's a present for you on the table.
   .... it and see what it is.

6 After I do the vacuuming, I always
   .... the vacuum cleaner.

6 ⭐⭐⭐ What jobs do you do at home? Complete
the questions then answer them so they are true
for you.

1 A Do you do the washing-up at home ?
   B Yes, every day.

2 A How often .... ?
   B ....

3 A Do you ever .... ?
   B ....

4 A When do you .... ?
   B ....

can / can't

1 ✪ **Choose the correct words.**

1 We (can) / **can't to** watch TV in the evenings.
2 He **can plays** / **can't play** football in the garden.
3 They **can to** / **can't have** dinner in their bedrooms.
4 You **don't can** / **can't** use your father's computer.
5 She **can** / **not can** eat in front of the TV on Wednesday nights.
6 I **can** / **don't can** watch DVDs at the weekends.

2 ✪✪ **Write a question for each sentence in exercise 1.**

1 _Can we watch TV in the evenings?_
2 ....
3 ....
4 ....
5 ....
6 ....

have to / don't have to

3 ✪✪ **Read the 'Summer Camp jobs' notice and complete the text message with *have to* or *don't have to*.**

Summer Camp jobs

Every day:
Make your bed, tidy your room and put away your clothes.

Friday:
Do the vacuuming and take out the rubbish.

After meals:
Clear the table and load the dishwasher.

Note:
Every day, the house leader makes breakfast, lunch and dinner.

4 ✪✪ **Complete the sentences about the text in exercise 3. Use the information in brackets.**

1 Tom _has to help with the housework._ (housework)
2 Tom .... (breakfast)
3 The house leader .... (lunch)
4 Tom and his friends .... (the table)
5 The house leader .... (vacuuming)
6 Tom and his friends .... (washing-up)

5 ✪✪✪ **What are the rules at your house? Write sentences.**

I can …
    I can eat in front of the TV.
1 ....
2 ....

I can't …
3 ....
4 ....

I have to …
5 ....
6 ....

I don't have to …
7 ....
8 ....

.ıll 🔋 12:31

Dear Mum and Dad,

I like summer camp, but I **1** _have to_ help with the housework. Every day I **2** .... make my bed, tidy my room and put away my clothes. But I **3** .... make meals. The house leader does that. After meals, my friends and I **4** .... clear the table and load the dishwasher. We **5** .... help with the washing-up.

On Friday, I **6** .... do the vacuuming and I also **7** .... take out the rubbish.

Love,

Tom

Vocabulary

Hobbies

1 ⭐ **Match the hobbies 1–8 with the pictures A–H.**

1 bake cakes ....C....
2 collect coins ....
3 go deep-sea fishing ....
4 go online ....
5 go to the gym ....
6 make videos ....
7 play golf ....
8 write a blog ....

A
B
C
D
E
F
G
H

2 ✪✪ **Complete the sentences with the hobbies from exercise 1.**

1 Fahad's dad uses a boat for his hobby. He
   goes deep-sea fishing .
2 My hobby is good for keeping fit.
   I ....
3 Bill does his hobby in the kitchen.
   He ....
4 Liz uses a camera for her hobby.
   She ....
5 Emir and Yusuf's hobby is a type of
   communication. They use a computer
   to ....
6 Aleena's hobby is using the internet. She
   .... every day to do shopping.
7 My dad's hobby uses a ball.
   He ....
   ....
8 Phil has a lot of foreign money because he
   .... as a hobby.

3 ✪✪ **Complete the blog with the hobbies from exercise 1.**

Blogger

Hobbies and today's youth

We often read that young people today **¹** _go online_ every day for hours, spend a lot of time text messaging their friends, and don't have any other interests or hobbies. I don't think it's true. Let me explain. OK, I use the internet every day because I **²** .... about my daily life, and I do it after I finish my school work, but I also like to keep fit. I **³** .... every week, and I'm not alone – lots of young people do it. My friend Cathy sometimes goes online, but she doesn't chat with friends or play games. She buys and sells foreign money on the internet because she **⁴** .... My friend Marian is in the kitchen every day. Why? Because she **⁵** .... She wants to have a restaurant someday. She also **⁶** .... of her hobby and puts them on the internet to teach people about baking. I've got one more example. My friend Sue **⁷** .... almost every week because her father has a boat. And every year she goes on holiday with her father to **⁸** .... Sometimes, they enter competitions, because they're very good at the game. So yes, young people use the internet, but lots of us have other interesting hobbies as well.

4 ✪✪✪ **Write a short blog about your favourite hobby. Answer the questions below in your blog.**

1 What's your hobby?
2 Where do you do it?
3 How often do you do it?
4 Why do you enjoy it?

Verb + -ing

1 ⭐⭐ Complete the forum with the -ing form of the verbs below.

buy   collect   eat   get up   go
play   read   study   ~~watch~~

Teen Forums

Tell us about the things you really love and hate.

I love football. I love ¹ _watching_ it on TV and I love ² .... it with my friends.

I can't stand ³ .... shopping for clothes. It takes all day just to buy one thing. But I don't mind ⁴ .... clothes on the internet.

Kevin, UK

· ·

I love ⁵ .... Italian food – pizza, pasta, risotto. It's the best food in the world!

I don't mind ⁶ .... at school, but when I'm at home I prefer relaxing – and eating!

Basma, United Arab Emirates

· ·

I just absolutely love ⁷ .... books. I also like ⁸ .... them. I've got over 100.

And one thing I hate? I absolutely hate ⁹ .... early in the morning at the weekend.

Jane, US

2 ⭐⭐ Complete the sentences. Use the correct form of the verbs *love, like, don't mind, don't like* or *hate*, and the -ing form of the verbs in brackets.

1 My dad _loves reading_ the newspaper in the morning. (☺☺ read)

2 Amber .... at the weekend. (☹☹ do the vacuuming)

3 Talib .... football after school. (☺ play)

4 My sisters .... the washing-up after lunch. (☹ do)

5 Dave .... the gym every weekend. (☺☺ go to)

6 My mother .... cakes. (☺ bake)

7 I .... the dishwasher. (☹☹ unload)

8 You .... English. (☺ study)

3 ⭐⭐⭐ Write six sentences that are true for you. Use the words below and a verb + -ing.

can't stand   don't like   don't mind   hate   like   love

1 ....
2 ....
3 ....
4 ....
5 ....
6 ....

would like to

4 ⭐⭐ Look at the information in the chart. Complete the sentences with *would like to* or *wouldn't like to* and the correct form of the verb.

Would you like to … ?	Kevin	Basma	Jane
learn a new language	✗	✓	✓
work abroad	✓	✗	✓
travel around the world	✓	✓	✗
write a book	✗	✓	✓

1 Kevin _wouldn't like to learn_ a new language.
2 Basma and Jane .... a book.
3 Jane .... around the world.
4 Kevin .... abroad.
5 Basma .... abroad.
6 Kevin .... around the world.
7 Basma and Jane .... a new language.
8 Kevin .... a book.

5 ⭐⭐⭐ Answer the questions about yourself. Write full answers.

1 Would you like to learn a new language? Why / Why not?
....

2 Would you like to work abroad? Why / Why not?
....

3 Would you like to travel around the world? Why / Why not?
....

4 Would you like to write a book? Why / Why not?
....

Writing

An internet profile

LANGUAGE FOCUS | **Capital letters and punctuation**

1 ✪ **Correct the spelling, punctuation or use of capital letters in the sentences.**

1 He doesnt like doing the washing-up.   doesn't
2 Her name is jane and she's from London.   ....
3 Im mad about shopping.   ....
4 They live with there parents.   ....
5 Were big fans of Chinese food.   ....
6 Samir likes playing football on saturdays.   ....
7 does Salina like baking cakes?   ....
8 I don't like doing the Vacuuming.   ....

2 ✪✪ **Rewrite the sentences using capital letters and punctuation in the correct places.**

1 i dont mind doing the washing-up

2 samira doesnt like watching american TV shows

3 my name is laila and ive got collections of japanese chinese and russian coins

TASK | **Internet profile**

3 ✪ **Read the notes about Andy and complete the profile.**

Name:	Andy
Home:	New York City, US
Lives with:	mother, father and sister Emma
Likes:	studying French – enjoys reading French comic books (has a collection), making dinner – his favourite is French food
Dislikes:	doing the vacuuming, clothes shopping
Weekend hobbies:	going to the gym, playing golf
Would like to:	meet someone from France or Canada to email in French

About   Photos   Friends

✉ **Message**   ☐ **Add photos**

My friend's name is ¹ _Andy_ and he's from New York City, in the US. He lives with his mother, ² .... and sister Emma.

Andy is really into studying ³ .... He enjoys reading French ⁴ .... and he has a collection of them. He also likes making ⁵ .... His favourite type of food is ⁶ .... food – for cooking and for eating!

He doesn't like housework, and he really can't stand doing the ⁷ .... He also hates ⁸ .... – his sister Emma asks him to go with her, but he always has an excuse.

Andy is really into keeping ⁹ .... He spends a lot of time playing ¹⁰ .... and going to the gym at weekends.

He would like to meet someone from ¹¹ .... or France. He would also like to email in ¹² .... and learn more about French food!

4 ✪✪✪ **Write an internet profile of your friend. Use the profile in exercise 3 as a model.**

• Write notes about your friend for each paragraph:
  Paragraph 1: About your friend
  Paragraph 2: Your friend's likes
  Paragraph 3: Your friend's dislikes
  Paragraph 4: Your friend's hobbies
  Paragraph 5: Things your friend would like to do
• Write 100–150 words.

Review Unit 2 in the Student's Book and complete the exercises below. Think about your progress and choose one of the faces.

READING — Different lives

1 Read the text on page 19 of the Student's Book again. Answer the questions.

1 Find words in the text for the following definitions:
- to come together ....
- a person with no siblings ....
- a child with no parents ....

2 Tick (✓) the correct answers.
Who lives in the biggest household?
a Salim ☐ **b** Diah ☐ **c** Katy and Sarah ☐

Who lives in the smallest household?
a Salim ☐ **b** Diah ☐ **c** Katy and Sarah ☐

Which household is the most like yours? Why?

....
....

I can understand a text about family life.

☹ 😐 🙂

VOCABULARY

2 Who usually does these jobs in your family? Use the words in brackets and the correct verb from exercise 1 on page 20 of the Student's Book.

.... (dinner)
.... (washing-up)
.... (rubbish)
.... (dishwasher)
.... (vacuuming)

I can talk about helping at home.

☹ 😐 🙂

3 Match the two halves of the hobbies. Then answer the question.

1 collect   a gym
2 bake   b videos
3 go to the   c a blog
4 go deep-sea   d coins
5 make   e cakes
6 write   f fishing

Which hobby would you like to take up? Why?

....
....

I can talk about hobbies.

☹ 😐 🙂

GRAMMAR

4 Complete the sentences with *can, can't, have to* or *don't have to*.

There are some rules at home I ¹................ follow. I ²................ play football in the park because the park is near my house, but I ³................ go shopping with my friends because the shopping centre is very far away. There are some jobs that I ⁴................ do at home: every day I make my bed and tidy my room. I ⁵................ do the vacuuming because my brother does it.

I can talk about permission and obligation.

☹ 😐 🙂

5 Correct the mistakes. Then rewrite the sentences in the opposite negative form.

1 I love bakeing cakes. ....
....

2 I like traveling by bus. ....
....

3 I love collectting coins. ....
....

4 I'd like to studying abroad. ....
....

I can talk about things I like doing.

☹ 😐 🙂

SPEAKING

6 Number the conversation in the correct order 1–7.

.... **Suzy** Hey, Tina, look at this.

.... **Suzy** Don't you like it? I think it's really cool.

.... **Tina** What?

.... **Tina** It's OK, I suppose.

.... **Suzy** What do you think of this watch?

.... **Suzy** Hmm, maybe you're right.

.... **Tina** I prefer it in black.

I can ask for and give opinions.

☹ 😐 🙂

1 Read the texts and look at the photos. Match the texts 1–4 with the photos A–D.

My family

B

1 C

This is my brother. He loves playing football and also playing golf with my dad. At home he helps clear the table and takes out the rubbish. He'd like to be a famous footballer!

2

This is my dad. He likes playing golf and watching football on TV. He'd like to try deep-sea fishing. At home he loads and unloads the dishwasher. Sometimes he makes dinner. He doesn't like doing the washing-up!

D

3

This is me. I like baking cakes and making dinner, and I also like reading books in English. At home I tidy the house and help my mum make dinner, and I don't mind doing the washing-up sometimes. I'd like to study abroad and improve my English.

4

This is my mum. She likes making videos of our family and studying English. She'd like to go on holiday to New York City. At home she makes the meals and does the vacuuming. She doesn't like loading and unloading the dishwasher.

2 Make a poster about your family or someone else's family. Follow the steps in the project checklist.

- For each member of the family, write about their hobbies, the jobs that they do at home, and the things that they like, dislike, or don't mind doing.
- Find or draw pictures of each member of the family. If you want, do more than one picture for each person.
- Make a large poster that introduces the family. Write the information next to the pictures.

TALK ABOUT IT

3 Exchange your family poster with your classmates. How are the family members similar? How are they different?

> Our brothers both like studying English.

> My mum always loads the dishwasher, but Tom's mum never does it.

My charity expedition: Saturday, 19th July

19th July: I'm in Tanzania, in Africa, on a charity
¹ <u>expedition</u> . I'm trekking on Mount Kilimanjaro in aid
of the International Children's Hospital. The trip is ten days
long and the trekking is very ² .... !

Today's blog is about Charity Expeditions, the company
I'm travelling with in Tanzania. It's a British company.

What does the company do?

Charity Expeditions organises travel adventure holidays
for young people and students. They have 25 years'
experience in taking school groups on expeditions all
over the world ³ .... charities.

Where do they usually go?

All over the world! Here are some trips they make every year:

- They travel to China and walk 100 kilometres along the Great Wall.

- They go to Vietnam and Cambodia, where they cycle 600 kilometres from Ho Chi Minh City to Angkor Wat.

- They go to France, where the group climbs to the top of Mont Blanc, the famous 4810–metre mountain. The climb usually takes three days.

- They take groups to the jungles of Malaysia, Indonesia and Brazil. Here they do a ⁴ .... of the local area and ⁵ .... the number of tourists visiting the area.

How does adventure travel make money for charity?

Friends and family ⁶ .... young adventurers. When a young person completes a trekking, climbing or cycling expedition, people give money to charity. My friends and family are giving the International Children's Hospital more than £1200 for my trek!

Thank you for reading my blog!

Mike

Posted by **Mike Jones** at 11.50

---

1 ✪ **Complete the blog with six of the words or phrases below.**

| challenging | charity | ~~expedition~~ | in aid of |
| memorable | monitor | sponsor | survey |

2 ✪ **Read Mike's blog again. Which country is not mentioned?**

a China b Malaysia c Canada

3 ✪✪ **Choose the correct answers.**

1 Mike is on an expedition in (Africa)/ China.

2 Charity Expeditions is a company from the UK / Tanzania.

3 The company takes tourists on trekking holidays / takes students on journeys.

4 Students go cycling / walking in China.

5 In Malaysia, students record information about the tourists / visit popular tourist areas.

6 The International Children's Hospital gives money to Mike / gets money from Mike's friends and family.

4 ✪✪ **Complete the sentences with the numbers below.**

| ~~10~~ 25 100 600 1200 4810 |

1 Mike's trip in Tanzania is 10 days long.

2 His family will give £ .... to charity.

3 Mont Blanc is .... metres high.

4 The walk along the Great Wall is .... kms long.

5 The cycle ride in Vietnam and Cambodia is .... kms long.

6 Charity Expeditions has .... years' experience in organising on adventure trips.

5 ✪✪✪ **Answer the questions.**

1 Why is Mike trekking in Africa?

2 How does Charity Expeditions make money for charity?

3 Which of the adventure trips in the blog would you like to go on? Why?

4 What is your most memorable travel experience?

Vocabulary

Holiday activities

1 ⭐ **Look at the pictures. Complete the sentences with the activities below.**

> backpacking   buying souvenirs   ~~chilling out~~
> eating out   scuba diving   sightseeing   trekking
> visiting relatives

1   They're chilling out .

2   He's ....

3   She's ....
....

4   They're ....
....

5   He's ....
....

6   They're ....
....

7   She's ....
....

8   They're ....
....

2 ⭐⭐ **Complete the sentences with the activities in exercise 1.**

1   Every year, they go to Malaysia's unspoilt coast. They like scuba diving in the water there.

2   We often go to restaurants because we love
....

3   He doesn't want to walk around the city because he can't stand ....

4   I hate carrying my things on my back. I don't like ....

5   I always go to the shops when I travel because I like ....

6   We go to see my grandmother every week. I like ....

7   Our holidays are usually in the mountains because we like ....

8   My favourite activity on holiday is sitting in a café, reading a book and ....

VOCABULARY BUILDER	collocations with *make* and *do*

3 ⭐⭐ **Complete the text with *make* or *do* and the words below.**

> a course   a list   noise   nothing   plans   ~~research~~

Every summer my family go on a summer holiday, and every year it's different. We all ¹ do research on the internet for new ideas. Then, we all ² .... of five or six things we want to do. Every year, one item on my list is 'go to the beach and ³ ....', which really means chill out, relax and read books. However, we usually choose something very active. We decide to ⁴ ...., for example French or Spanish, or even go scuba diving. After we decide what to do, we work together to ⁵ .... for the holiday. Where will we go exactly? How many days will we stay there? What will we eat? Sometimes we need to make rules, too. My little brother likes to wake up very early, so we have a holiday rule: you can't ⁶ .... before 8 o'clock in the morning. That's quiet time!

4 ⭐⭐⭐ **Write sentences about the holiday activities in exercise 1 that are true for you. Use *love, like, don't mind* and *can't stand*.**

> I love scuba diving. I like seeing the different fish.

1   ....

2   ....

3   ....

Present continuous: positive and negative

1 ✪ **Match the pairs of sentences.**

1 Kevin isn't sightseeing. He's working.   *e*
2 Emir is chilling out.
3 Tom isn't scuba diving.
4 Ed is eating out.
5 Fahad isn't buying souvenirs.
6 It isn't raining.

a The sun is shining.
b He doesn't like cooking dinner at home.
c He's on holiday.
d He can't stand swimming, or water!
e He's a tourist guide.
f He doesn't like shopping.

2 ✪✪ **Complete the email with the positive or negative present continuous form of the verbs in brackets.**

Hi Lana,

Just a quick email to say hello from the UK.
We ¹ *'re having* (have) a wonderful visit. This time, we ² _____ (visit) London – we're staying in Oxford. We ³ _____ (have) a good time and the holiday is very relaxing.
We ⁴ _____ (stay) in a lovely, little hotel ten minutes from the city centre. At the moment, I ⁵ _____ (sit) in a café with my brother.
He ⁶ _____ (drink) a cup of English tea and I ⁷ _____ (have) coffee. Mum and Dad ⁸ _____ (do) some shopping. They ⁹ _____ (look) for souvenirs to take back home. Oh, and guess what? The weather is sunny! It ¹⁰ _____ (rain) today.

See you soon,

Cathy

3 ✪✪ **Rewrite the negative sentences in the positive form and the positive sentences in the negative form.**

1 We're trekking through a jungle in Malaysia.
   We aren't trekking through a jungle in Malaysia.
2 They're staying in London.

3 They aren't making plans for a holiday.

4 She's doing a Spanish course in Madrid.

5 I'm not having a good time in Istanbul.

6 I'm drinking coffee in a café.

7 He isn't swimming with dolphins in Florida.

8 You aren't cycling on the right road.

4 ✪✪ **Look at the photos. Write four positive and four negative sentences.**

Nasir

Suzy

Positive
1 Nasir *is sitting in a café.* (sit)
2 Nasir _____ (drink)
3 Suzy _____ (trek)
4 Suzy _____ (wear)
Negative
5 Suzy *isn't sitting in a café.* (sit)
6 Suzy _____ (drink)
7 Nasir _____ (trek)
8 Nasir _____ (wear)

5 ✪✪✪ **Write three positive and three negative sentences that are true for you. Use the present continuous.**

At the moment, I'm wearing jeans.

1 _____
2 _____
3 _____
4 _____
5 _____
6 _____

Geographical features

1 ⭐ Match the two halves of the names of famous geographical features.

1	Niagara	**a**	Valley
2	The Suez	**b**	River
3	Lake	**c**	Sea
4	The South	**d**	Falls
5	Death	**e**	Ocean
6	The Atlas	**f**	Canyon
7	The Zambezi	**g**	Rainforest
8	The Sahara	**h**	Canal
9	The Dead	**i**	Mountains
10	The Grand	**j**	Pole
11	The Pacific	**k**	Malawi
12	The Amazon	**l**	Desert

2 ⭐⭐ Match the places in exercise 1 with the descriptions.

1 A man-made river: this connects the Mediterranean Sea with the Red Sea.
the Suez Canal

2 An area of low land in the mountains: this is a very hot place in California, in the US.

3 A large area of water: this is in Africa, between Tanzania, Malawi and Mozambique.

4 A large area of sand: this is a very hot, very dry place in North Africa.

5 There are lots of trees in this area. Most of this area is in Brazil.

6 A place where water drops over an edge: this is on a river between Canada and the US.

7 A big sea: North, Central and South America are on one side of this, and Asia and Australia are on the other.

8 These are very large rocks, like big hills. They are in Algeria, Morocco and Tunisia.

9 A very cold place in Antarctica.

10 A long, thin area of water: this is about 2500 kms long and ends in the Indian Ocean.

11 An area cut into the mountains by a river: this is in Arizona, in the US.

12 A very large area of water: fish can't live in the water because it's about 33% salt.

3 ⭐⭐ Do the quiz.

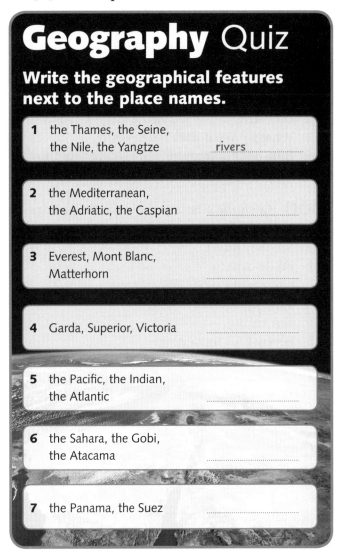

Geography Quiz

Write the geographical features next to the place names.

1 the Thames, the Seine, the Nile, the Yangtze — rivers

2 the Mediterranean, the Adriatic, the Caspian

3 Everest, Mont Blanc, Matterhorn

4 Garda, Superior, Victoria

5 the Pacific, the Indian, the Atlantic

6 the Sahara, the Gobi, the Atacama

7 the Panama, the Suez

4 ⭐⭐⭐ Answer the questions about the places in exercise 1.

1 Which place is good for trekking and climbing?
The Atlas Mountains are good for trekking and climbing.

2 Which place is good for scuba diving?

3 Which place do you think is the most beautiful?

4 Which place is good for seeing different plants and animals?

5 Which place would you most like to visit?

Present continuous: questions

1 ✪ **Choose the correct words.**

1 **What** / **Where** are you doing?
2 Are you **stay** / **staying** in Oxford at the moment?
3 Is Ahmed **trekking** / **treks** in the Atlas Mountains this week?
4 **Do** / **Are** Fatima and Nadia visiting family?
5 **What's** / **What does** Jenna doing?
6 **How often** / **Why** are you reading about the Sahara Desert?

2 ✪✪ **Match the answers a–f with the questions 1–6 in exercise 1.**

a No, they aren't.   4
b No, he isn't. ....
c I'm reading about scuba diving. ....
d She's sightseeing in London. ....
e Yes, we are. ....
f Because it's interesting. ....

3 ✪✪ **Look at the list of students and activities. Write questions and answers in the present continuous. Use the words in brackets.**

Students travelling this week

Jamal – Malaysian jungle trek

Omar – Australian scuba diving course

Yasmin – Kenya mountain trek

Kevin – Paris sightseeing

Liz – Cairo sightseeing

1 Jamal (trek)
  A Where 's Jamal trekking?
  B He's trekking in the Malaysian jungle.
2 Omar (learn)
  A What .... ?
  B ....
3 Yasmin (cycle)
  A Is .... ?
  B ....
4 Kevin and Liz (do)
  A What .... ?
  B ....
5 Liz (visit Paris)
  A Is .... ?
  B ....

4 ✪✪✪ **Answer the questions about yourself. Use the present continuous.**

1 Where are you studying at the moment?
....

2 How are you feeling?
....

3 What is your father / mother / brother / sister doing at the moment?
....

Present simple and present continuous

5 ✪✪ **Complete the diary entry with the correct form of the present simple or present continuous.**

25TH APRIL

This week, I [1] 'm (be) on an adventure holiday with my class. Every year, the school [2] .... (go) on a trip. This year, we [3] .... (trek) in the Atlas Mountains in aid of charity. Our friends and families [4] .... (sponsor) us to do the trek. We [5] .... (not raise) money for one charity – each student [6] .... (trek) in aid of a different charity. Every day, our guide [7] .... (teach) us a lot about the natural world and about climbing. At home, I usually [8] .... (use) my mobile phone every day, but this week I [9] .... (not use) it at all. I didn't bring it. It [10] .... (be) very peaceful out here!

6 ✪✪✪ **Answer the questions about yourself. Use the present simple.**

1 What do you usually do at weekends?
....
....

2 What do you usually wear at weekends?
....
....

3 What household jobs do you usually do?
....
....

A holiday email

LANGUAGE FOCUS | *and, but, because* and *so*

1 ✪✪ **Complete the sentences with *and, but, because* or *so*.**

1 I've got an exam tomorrow, _so_ I'm studying hard.
2 We're having lunch early _____ we're all really hungry.
3 It's late, _____ I'm not tired.
4 It's raining, _____ we're not going outside.
5 We're not going outside _____ it's raining.
6 I like scuba diving _____ swimming.

2 ✪✪✪ **Complete the sentences. Use your own ideas.**

1 For lunch I want a sandwich and _____ .
2 I like some sports, but _____ .
3 I'm studying hard because _____ .
4 That café is expensive, so _____ .
5 I don't want to go to bed because _____ .
6 I'm tired, but _____ .

TASK | **Holiday email**

3 ✪✪ **Complete the email with the words below.**

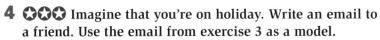

| chilling out | course | ~~holiday~~ | hotel | shining | sightseeing | sitting | swimming | time | trekking |

Hi Adam,

Just a quick email to say hello from Langkawi, in Malaysia. I'm here on ¹ _holiday_ with Mum, Dad and Amber and we're having a fantastic ² _____ . Malaysia is an amazing country! At the moment, I'm ³ _____ in an internet café. The sun is ⁴ _____ and the weather is hot.

We're staying in a spectacular ⁵ _____ near the beach. There are some really interesting places in the area, so we're travelling around and doing some ⁶ _____ . We're also ⁷ _____ at the hotel a lot and ⁸ _____ in the ocean every day.

There's a scuba diving school here, so I'd like to do a ⁹ _____ and learn to scuba dive! I'd also like to go ¹⁰ _____ through the rainforest and climb the Gunung Mat Chinchang mountain.

See you soon,

Max

4 ✪✪✪ **Imagine that you're on holiday. Write an email to a friend. Use the email from exercise 3 as a model.**

- Include three paragraphs. Answer these questions:
  Where are you?
  Where are you staying?
  What would you like to do there?
- Write 100–150 words.

Review Unit 3 in the Student's Book and complete the exercises below. Think about your progress and choose one of the faces.

READING Go, go, go!

1 **Read the text on page 29 of the Student's Book again. Answer the questions.**

1 Find words in the text for the following definitions:
- to watch and study ....
- long journey ....
- to help (something) ....

2 What can people learn in Malaysia's jungle?
....

3 What can teenagers do in the Red Sea?
....

4 What event is Jack King taking part in?
....

I can understand a text about unusual holidays.

VOCABULARY

2 **Complete the holiday activities. Then answer the questions.**

| diving   out   out   packing   relatives   souvenirs |

1 back ....   4 eating ....
2 buying ....   5 scuba ....
3 chilling ....   6 visiting ....

Which of the activities would you like to do? Where would you do it? Write a sentence.
....

I can talk about things to do on holiday.

3 **Match the geographical features with the definitions. Then answer the question.**

| canal   desert   falls   lake   rainforest |

1 A large area of sand ....
2 An area with lots of trees and plants
....
3 A place where a river drops over a mountain edge ....
4 Quite a big area of water ....
5 A man-made river ....

Name a famous geographical feature. Where is it?

I can talk about places in the world.

GRAMMAR

4 **Complete the sentences with the present continuous form of the words in brackets.**

1 We .... (not trek) in Malaysia.
2 Amira and Helen aren't at home.
   They .... (eat out) tonight.
3 I .... (cycle) through Laos now.
4 It .... (not rain) today.
5 She .... (not buying) souvenirs – she's having lunch.

I can describe what is happening now.

5 **Choose the correct words to complete each question. Then answer the questions.**

1 **Do you go / Are you going** on holiday every year with your family?
....

2 What **do you do / are you doing** at the moment?
....

3 **Do you study / Are you studying** English every day?
....

4 When **do you usually start / are you usually starting** school in the morning?
....

I can talk about routines and things in progress.

SPEAKING

6 **Complete the conversation.**

Rob   Excuse me. ¹................ ? I'm looking for the Island Scuba Diving School.

Hassan Ah yes, it's on the beach at Turtle Bay.
        ²................ ?

Rob   Not really, no.

Hassan Let me show you on the map. It's here, look.

Rob   OK, great. ³................ ?

Hassan Erm, there are some restaurants in Bay Street.

Rob   ⁴................ ?

Hassan ⁵................ ?

Rob   Yes.

Hassan Well, it's about ten minutes' walk.

Rob   Brilliant. Thanks very much.

I can ask for information about a place.

1 In *Sherlock Holmes and the Sport of Kings*, Silver Blaze is a race horse and John Straker is his trainer. Read the first extract. Answer the questions.

1 What time did John Straker get out of bed?

2 Why did he want to look around the stables?

3 Who or what was missing the next morning?

4 What happened to John Straker?

2 Answer the questions about the first extract. Use your own words and ideas.

1 Why do you think John Straker was worried about a stranger at the stables?

2 Why do you think Silver Blaze wasn't in his stable?

3 How do you think John Straker died?

3 Read what happens next in the paragraph below. Why do the police think the stranger killed Straker?

When they found Straker, he had a cut in his leg and his head was badly hurt. He had a small knife in his right hand and a red and black scarf in his left hand … it was the stranger's scarf! The local police think that the stranger, Fitzroy Simpson, killed Straker.

4 The great detective, Sherlock Holmes, doesn't agree with the police. Read the paragraph below to find out part of what he thinks. What do you think happened next?

John Straker didn't want Silver Blaze to win the horse race, for the Wessex Cup, so he took the horse out on to the moors to cut one of his legs, so it would lose. But Silver Blaze got frightened …

5 Read the second extract to find out what Holmes thinks happened. Who or what killed Straker?

1

The next thing happened at one o'clock in the morning when John Straker got out of bed.

'What's the matter?' said his wife. 'Where are you going?'

'To the stables,' Straker said. 'I can't stop thinking about that stranger. I just want to have a look around.'

'But it's raining. Wait until the rain stops,' she said.

'No, no,' Straker said. 'I want to go now.'

He left the house and Mrs Straker went back to sleep. At seven in the morning she woke up, but her husband was not there. She quickly got up, called the servant, Edith, and they ran down to the stables.

They found the stables unlocked. Straker was not there, and inside, on a chair, Ned Hunter slept like a dead man. Silver Blaze was gone, and his stable door was open. They called the other two boys from the room over the stables. They were good sleepers and heard nothing in the night.

Nobody could wake Ned Hunter, so the two women and the boys ran out to look for the trainer and the horse. Five hundred metres from the stables, they saw Straker's coat on a small tree. Down the hill, just past the tree, they found the trainer. He was dead.

2

'And on Monday night, out on the moor,' said Mr Ross, 'what happened, do you think?'

'How about this?' said Holmes. 'Straker takes the horse down the hill. He sees Simpson's scarf on the ground, and takes it with him – why, I don't know. He puts his coat on a tree, gets out the candle and the matches, and the knife, and begins his work. But Silver Blaze doesn't like it. Perhaps he's afraid, perhaps he feels something is wrong. He's a big, strong horse, and he gets angry. He kicks out with his back legs, and the horseshoes hit Straker on the head. Straker goes down, into the mud, and the knife in his hand goes into his own leg. The horse disappears into the night.'

From *Sherlock Holmes and the Sport of Kings*, Oxford Bookworms. Retold by Jennifer Bassett.

How healthy is your lifestyle?

I think I'm quite healthy and fit. I never eat **¹** junk food .
I don't eat fattening snacks or too much sugar. I don't eat
too much meat, and my mum makes nutritious meals
with lots of vegetables. I'm an active person and I like
doing outdoor things like trekking and cycling. I often go
to the mountains with my parents at the weekends with
our bikes. We sometimes cycle 30 kilometres or more.
Dave (16 years old)

I like to go to the gym and I go swimming three times a week.
I sometimes swim in competitions. I'm never in a **²**＿＿＿＿ when I
exercise. I use a lot of **³**＿＿＿＿ so I eat quite a healthy diet. Before
competitions, I always eat plenty of vegetables and I don't eat too much junk food.
But I do eat a bit too much chocolate!
I eat a little every day. I think I have a chocolate **⁴**＿＿＿＿ ! If you want to be fit and healthy, you need to
make an effort.
Karen (15 years old)

To be honest, my lifestyle isn't very healthy at all and I guess I'm not very fit. I never eat fruit and I hardly ever eat
vegetables. I just don't like them. I love food like pizza and burgers and snacks, like crisps. So I'm a bit overweight
and I guess there's a **⁵**＿＿＿＿ vitamins in my diet. I generally do my homework in the evenings after dinner and
I often go to bed late, so I don't get enough sleep. I occasionally play football, but I don't think I do enough exercise.
But I do a lot of mental exercise – I love playing computer games. I never sit at home and do nothing.
Sam (17 years old)

1 ✪ **Complete the article with five of the words or phrases below.**

| addiction | average | bad mood | documentary |
| energy | experiment | ~~junk food~~ | lack of |

2 ✪ **Read the article again and complete the sentences with the correct names.**

1 ＿＿＿＿＿＿＿＿＿＿ has an unhealthy lifestyle and an unhealthy diet.

2 ＿＿＿＿＿＿＿＿＿＿ has a healthy lifestyle and an OK diet.

3 ＿＿＿＿＿＿＿＿＿＿ has a healthy lifestyle and a healthy diet.

3 ✪✪ **Read the article again. Write *true* or *false*. Correct the false sentences.**

1 Dave occasionally eats junk food.

＿＿＿＿＿＿

2 Dave never eats meat. ＿＿＿＿

3 Karen likes swimming. ＿＿＿＿

4 Karen never eats chocolate. ＿＿＿＿

5 Sam is always busy when he's at home.

＿＿＿＿＿＿

4 ✪✪✪ **Answer the questions.**

1 What is healthy about Dave's diet?

＿＿＿＿＿＿＿＿＿＿＿＿＿＿＿＿＿

2 How does Dave keep fit?

＿＿＿＿＿＿＿＿＿＿＿＿＿＿＿＿＿

3 How does exercise make Karen feel?

＿＿＿＿＿＿＿＿＿＿＿＿＿＿＿＿＿

4 Why does Karen say she has a chocolate addiction?

＿＿＿＿＿＿＿＿＿＿＿＿＿＿＿＿＿

5 Why is Sam overweight?

＿＿＿＿＿＿＿＿＿＿＿＿＿＿＿＿＿

6 Why does Sam often go to bed late?

＿＿＿＿＿＿＿＿＿＿＿＿＿＿＿＿＿

5 ✪✪✪ **Answer the questions.**

1 What healthy foods do you eat?

＿＿＿＿＿＿＿＿＿＿＿＿＿＿＿＿＿

2 What junk foods do you eat?

＿＿＿＿＿＿＿＿＿＿＿＿＿＿＿＿＿

3 How do you keep fit?

＿＿＿＿＿＿＿＿＿＿＿＿＿＿＿＿＿

Vocabulary

Health and diet

1 ✪ **Complete the definitions with the words below.**

~~calories~~ carbohydrates fattening fit nutritious overweight protein salty sugar vitamins

1 Fast food usually contains too many _calories_ .
2 Fruit is a good source of ....
3 Desserts are often ....
4 Growing teenagers should eat .... meals.
5 Meat is a good source of ....
6 To be ...., you need a good diet and lots of exercise.
7 Fructose is a type of ....
8 Potatoes and pasta contain ....
9 Crisps are often very ....
10 Fast food can make you ....

2 ✪✪ **Read the *Lifestyle Quiz* and choose the correct words to complete the questions. Then answer the questions. Check your answers in the key.**

Lifestyle Quiz

1 What percentage of British teenagers are (overweight)/ carbohydrates?
a 15%   **b** 25%   **c** 35%

2 How many portions of fruit and vegetables do we need to eat each day for a **vitamins / nutritious** diet?
a three   **b** four   **c** five

3 Which of the following is the most **fattening / fit**?
a mineral water
b fish
c chocolate

4 What is the recommended number of **calories / vitamins** per day for a woman?
a 1000   **b** 2000   **c** 3000

5 Which food is the highest in **nutritious / carbohydrates**?
a rice
b apple
c green salad

6 How many teaspoons of **sugar / salty** are there in the average can of cola?
a three   **b** eight   **c** 12

Key

| 1 c | 2 c | 3 c | 4 b | 5 a | 6 b |

3 ✪✪ **Complete the text with the words from exercise 1.**

Famous and Fit – Usain Bolt
Usain Bolt: Eating like a champion

It's important for Usain Bolt to stay ¹ fit . This includes training six days a week, but it also means eating like a champion. Usain has a very ² .... diet of traditional Jamaican food – chicken, which is a good source of ³ ...., rice, which is full of ⁴ .... and peas. He also eats a lot of bananas, which are a good source of ⁵ .... B and C. When Usain runs, his body uses a huge amount of energy. Bolt ate more than 5000 ⁶ .... per day during the Beijing Olympics – about twice the recommended amount for men. He's able to eat large amounts of foods that can be ⁷ .... – chicken nuggets, for example. But he isn't ⁸ .... because when he runs, his body uses a huge amount of energy. A champion also needs to eat some ⁹ .... foods because during exercise, the body loses a lot of salt through sweating. In general, though, he avoids foods that contain a lot of ¹⁰ ....

VOCABULARY BUILDER | **Phrases with prepositions**

4 ✪✪ **Complete the text with phrases made from a word from each box.**

~~according~~ average instead their opinion

in of on ~~to~~

¹ According to the World Health Organisation, an unhealthy diet causes a lot of illness around the world. ² ...., entire nations – and not just individuals – need to eat better. ³ ...., 2.8 million adults die each year because they are overweight. They recommend ⁴ .... eating so many unhealthy, fattening foods, people need to eat more fruit and vegetables.

5 ✪✪✪ **Write three sentences about the health and diet of your friends and family.**

1 ....
2 ....
3 ....

Comparatives and superlatives

1 ⭐ **Choose the correct words.**

1 Meals at home are usually (more) / **most** nutritious than fast food.

2 The **quick** / **quickest** way to get fit is to eat well and exercise.

3 I'm sure my brother is **fit** / **fitter** than I am because he does a lot of sport.

4 Which is the **most important** / **important** meal of the day?

5 I'd like to eat a **healthy** / **healthiest** diet, but it isn't easy.

6 For me, the **easiest** / **easier** way to exercise is walking to work.

7 I usually feel very **more tired** / **tired** at the end of the week.

2 ✪✪ **Complete the sentences with the words below.**

bad ~~best~~ better good worse worst

1 The _best_ food to eat before a race is pasta.

2 I always feel very relaxed after a ...., healthy meal.

3 In my opinion, the .... breakfast in the world is porridge. I hate it.

4 Three normal meals each day are .... than one big one.

5 Five cups of coffee for breakfast is bad, but eight cups is ....

6 I had a .... football match yesterday. We lost 4 to 1.

3 ✪✪ **Correct the mistakes in bold.**

1 My brother eats ~~quick~~ than everybody else in the family. _more quickly_

2 Burgers are the **more fattening** food I eat during the week. ....

3 Salad is **nutritious** than fries. ....

4 Fries from a fast food restaurant are usually very **most salty**. ....

5 My dad always likes a **nicest** cup of coffee in the morning. ....

6 Which athlete do you think is **the fitter**, an Olympic runner, an Olympic cyclist or an Olympic swimmer? ....

4 ✪✪ **Complete the text with the correct form of the words in brackets.**

Today's weather was ¹ _nicer_ (nice) than yesterday's, so Kevin left the office and went to a café for lunch. He only had £7 in his pocket, so he chose his lunch carefully. He wanted the salad, which was the ² .... (nutritious) item on the menu, but it was also the ³ .... (expensive), so he ordered a bowl of vegetable rice. A bowl was ⁴ .... (cheap) than a plate, but the plate was ⁵ .... (large) than the bowl, and he felt quite hungry. He sometimes drinks cola with lunch, but he ordered water, because it's ⁶ .... (healthy) than a fizzy drink. For dessert, the chocolate cake looked a lot ⁷ .... (delicious) than the banana, but the cake was certainly ⁸ .... (fattening). He chose the banana. That was probably the ⁹ .... (good) decision because Kevin's a bit overweight!

5 ✪✪✪ **Write comparative sentences about the foods. Use the adjectives in brackets and the words below.**

apples biscuits burgers chocolate fish fries porridge rice

1 .... (fattening)

2 .... (nutritious)

3 .... (sweet)

4 .... (healthy)

6 ✪✪✪ **Write two comparative and two superlative sentences about foods you sometimes eat.**

1 ....

....

2 ....

....

3 ....

....

4 ....

....

Vocabulary

School lunch

1 ✪ **Put the words below into the correct categories in the chart.**

| baked potato | ~~burger and fries~~ | chocolate muffin | cola | fried rice |
| fruit smoothie | mineral water | tomato salad | tuna wrap | vegetable soup |

hot food	cold food	desserts	drinks
burger and fries			

2 ✪✪ **Complete the** *Food and Drink Quiz* **with food and drink from exercise 1.**

Food and Drink Quiz

What are these foods and drinks?

1 A drink made from foods such as apples, bananas and oranges.
fruit smoothie

2 A good source of carbohydrates, often served with cheese.

3 A type of small, sweet cake.

4 A hot lunch, with no meat, served in a bowl.

5 A cold lunch made with tomatoes.

6 A cold lunch made of fish rolled in thin bread.

7 A drink, sometimes fizzy, with no calories and no colour.

8 A good source of carbohydrates, often served with Chinese food.

3 ✪✪ **Complete the text with the words below.**

baked potato	burgers	chocolate muffin
fried rice	fries	fruit	fruit smoothie
tomato salad	tuna wrap	~~vegetable soup~~

My brother's a vegetarian. He isn't a creative cook, so he eats ¹ vegetable soup every day. Of course he never eats ² .... because they have meat in them. He drinks a ³ .... every day, because he says it's the world's most nutritious drink. It's sometimes difficult for him when we go to a restaurant together. For his main course, he wants something hot, so he usually asks for a big ⁴ .... with cheese on top, or maybe a bowl of ⁵ .... Sometimes, though, the only hot vegetarian food available is an order of ⁶ .... – more potatoes! At lunch, I often order a ⁷ ...., but my brother doesn't eat fish, so that's no good for him. He can have a ⁸ .... though. It isn't hot, but it is nutritious. Desserts are easier. We both love sweet things so we often have a ⁹ ....
On days when we want a healthier option, ¹⁰ .... is a good choice.

5 ✪✪✪ **Complete the sentences so they are true for you. Write at least two things for each category.**

My favourite …
1 hot foods are ....
2 cold foods are ....
3 desserts are ....
4 drinks are ....

Foods that I don't like are …
5 ....
6 ....

some, any, much, many and a lot of

1 ✪✪ **Complete the text with the words below and *some* or *any*.**

> exercise   fruit   junk food   ~~meat~~
> pasta   restaurants   sweet things   vegetable

How do you stay fit and healthy?

I'm vegetarian. I don't eat [1] <u>any meat</u> or fish. I have a very healthy diet.
(Mike, UK)

I eat lots of fruit and vegetables. My mum makes sure we've always got [2] ...., such as apples and bananas, in the house.
(Hannah, Germany)

I usually eat healthy food, but sometimes I eat [3] .... – chocolate muffins, for example.
(Salina, Italy)

I never eat [4] .... like burgers and fries.
(Amy, Japan)

I don't know [5] .... that serve only vegetarian food. But most restaurants serve [6] .... dishes.
(Bill, US)

I usually have [7] .... and chicken before I go to the gym in the evening. I don't do [8] .... without eating a good source of protein and carbohydrates first. I need the energy.
(Omar, Egypt)

2 ✪✪ **Complete the questions with *How much* or *How many*.**

1   <u>How much</u> coffee do you drink?
2   .... fizzy drinks have we got?
3   .... sandwiches did you make?
4   .... coffee do you drink?
5   .... overweight people don't exercise?
6   .... money do you spend going to restaurants?
7   .... fruit do you eat?
8   .... times do you exercise each week?

too, too much, too many and (not) enough

3 ✪✪ **Rewrite the sentences with the word in brackets in the correct place.**

1   It's salty. (too)
    <u>It's too salty.</u>
2   I don't eat fruit. (enough)
    ....
3   He eats sweets. (too many)
    ....
4   Richard isn't fit. (enough)
    ....
5   There's food on my plate. (too much)
    ....
6   The food here is expensive. (too)
    ....
7   I haven't got money for a coffee. (enough)
    ....

4 ✪✪ **Correct the mistakes in bold.**

1   Don't eat **too much** chocolate muffins!
    <u>Don't eat too many chocolate muffins!</u>
2   We haven't got **not enough** food for lunch.
3   There are **too much** people here.
4   The soup is **too much** salty.
5   Do we have **enough of** fizzy drinks?
6   I eat **too many** chocolate, but I love it.
7   Is there **too many** meat for dinner tonight?
8   There's **enough** fruit for everyone, so we need to buy more.
9   Did you eat **too many** pizza?

5 ✪✪✪ **Complete the sentences. Use some of the words below, or your own ideas.**

> fattening foods   fish   fruit   meat   salt
> salty   sugar   sweet   vegetables   vitamins

1   I don't eat enough …
2   I probably eat too much …
3   I don't like foods that are too …
4   I probably eat too many …
5   I think I eat enough …

Writing

An opinion essay

1 ✪ **Number the paragraph topics below in the order 1–3 in which they appear in an opinion essay.**

☐ your opinions   ☐ conclusion   ☐ introduction

◖TASK│Opinion essay ▮ ▮ ▮ ▯

2 ✪✪ **Complete the gaps in the opinion essay with the missing sentences 1–3.**
1 In conclusion, the people and organisations, above all, play a very important part.
2 Thirdly, I think that food companies need to advertise responsibly.
3 To be fit and healthy, children and teenagers need to learn from other people, especially adults, what is and isn't a healthy diet.

Who is responsible for a child's diet?

As teenagers, we have more independence and we are more responsible for what we do. One important aspect of this is diet. ☐ In my opinion, the following people and organisations need to be responsible for educating children.

First and most importantly, I think it is the responsibility of parents to give their children a nutritious diet and to teach them about healthy eating. Next, schools need to provide healthier foods. Not only burgers and fries, but also vegetarian options, such as tomato salad or baked potatoes. Often, there aren't enough healthy choices in school. Dessert needs to include fruit salads, and not just chocolate muffins. Schools also need to include lessons about diet and nutrition. ☐ There are too many advertisements for salty foods and sweet things. TV advertisements have a lot of influence on children. Finally, it's important that television companies control the advertisements they show.

Of course, when children grow up they can then decide what to eat. However, it's important that they have the knowledge to make these decisions. ☐

3 ✪ **The essay contains some useful phrases for giving an opinion. Complete the sentences from the essay with the missing 'opinion' phrases.**
1 .... , the following people and organisations need to be responsible for educating children.
2 First and most importantly, ... it is the responsibility of parents to give their children a nutritious diet and to teach them about healthy eating.
3 Finally, ... television companies control the advertisements they show.
4 .... , the people and organisations above all play a very important part.

4 ✪✪✪ **Write an opinion essay that answers the question *What contributes to a healthy lifestyle?* Use the essay in exercise 2 as a model.**

- Include three paragraphs: introduction, your opinions, conclusion.
- Write 100–150 words.

4 | Self-evaluation

Review Unit 4 in the Student's Book and complete the exercises below. Think about your progress and choose one of the faces.

READING — A fast way to bad health

1 Read the text on page 37 of the Student's Book again. Answer the questions.

1 Find words in the text that are similar to the following words:
- test ....
- normal ....
- fast food ....

2 What were the negative effects of a junk food diet for Morgan Spurlock? Name three.
- ....
- ....
- ....

3 Give two reasons why junk food is bad for you.
- ....
- ....

I can understand a text about junk food.

VOCABULARY

2 Look again at exercise 1 on page 38 of the Student's Book. Circle the odd one out. Then use the circled word in a sentence.

1 salty   nutritious   (vitamins)
Fruit and vegetables contain lots of vitamins.

2 calories   overweight   fit
....

3 protein   carbohydrates   fattening
....

4 sugar   overweight   vitamins
....

5 nutritious   carbohydrates   calories
....

I can talk about health and diet.

3 Match the halves of the food words. Then answer the question.

1 baked   **a** water
2 fruit   **b** muffin
3 chocolate   **c** potato
4 tuna   **d** rice
5 mineral   **e** smoothie
6 fried   **f** wrap

What do you eat for lunch at school?

....

I can talk about school lunches.

GRAMMAR

4 Look at the photos and write sentences comparing the foods.

fish   burger   muffin

Comparatives
1 ....
2 ....
Superlatives
3 ....
4 ....

I can compare food.

5 How much of these foods do you eat? Write sentences using the words below and the foods in brackets.

| a lot   any   many   much   some |

1 I never eat any vegetables. (vegetables)
2 .... (sweet things)
3 .... (fruit)
4 .... (meat)
5 .... (junk food)

I can describe quantities.

SPEAKING

6 Write answers to the questions.

1 **A** What would you like?
   B I'd ....
2 **A** Anything else?
   B Yes, ...
3 **A** What sandwiches have you got?
   B We've ....
4 **A** How much is that?
   B That's ....

I can order food in a café.

1 Read the text. Then complete the food pyramid with the words in bold.

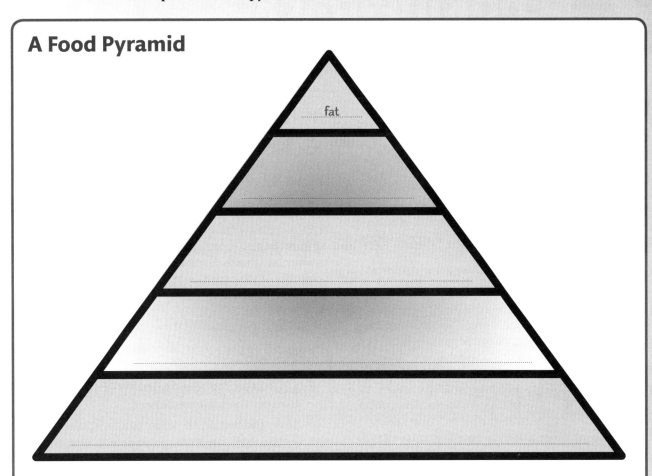

A Food Pyramid

fat

The food pyramid shows a nutritious diet. A healthy meal always includes a lot of **fruit and vegetables**. These basic foods are the most important, so they are at the bottom. This part of the pyramid is the widest, which shows that the biggest part of a healthy diet is fruit and vegetables. Next come **carbohydrates**. Foods such as potatoes and rice contain carbohydrates.

Protein is in the middle row. We shouldn't eat too much meat, but it's a good source of protein. Fish is, too. We shouldn't eat too much **sugar**, but a little is OK. **Fat** is actually much worse than sugar, which is why it's at the very top of the pyramid. But remember, some fat is an important part of a healthy diet.

2 Make a food pyramid poster. Follow the steps in the project checklist.

- Think of three or four examples of foods for each of the five parts of the pyramid. If you don't know the names in English, ask your teacher or use a dictionary.
- Find or draw pictures of each of the foods you listed.
- Make a large poster of the food pyramid. Write the food types in each level. Then write the names of the foods in the correct part of the pyramid.
- Now add the pictures of the foods in the correct places on the pyramid.

TALK ABOUT IT

3 Form a group and practise saying how often you eat the foods.

I eat rice every day.

I don't eat a lot of chocolate.

My mother cooks fish every Sunday.

4 Exchange your food pyramid poster with your classmates. What foods did they include?

Memory Humans versus animals by Kevin Coast

Who's got the best memory: humans or animals? It's an interesting question.

Several years ago, a group of scientists tested the [1] photographic memory of young chimpanzees. They showed chimpanzees and humans a computer screen with [2] .... on it. When the digits disappeared, the chimpanzees could remember the positions of the digits. In fact, they were better at this than the humans.

The scientists' experiments showed that a bird called the Clark's Nutcracker had a fantastic memory, too. The scientists watched the birds for months. They hid thousands of seeds over an area of about 20 square kilometres. Six months later, the birds found nearly all of the seeds from memory. Humans were far less successful at this type of activity.

Humans, however, can do something that animals can't do. We can decide how we want to [3] .... things. In the scientists' memory experiments, humans used different [4] .... to memorise objects. Some imagined pictures of the objects and some said the words to themselves again and again. The humans wrote lists and [5] .... their brains to remember important information. Animals can't do that!

1 ✪ Complete the text with five of the words or phrases below.

> digits   maximum   memorise   photographic memory
> recited   record   techniques   trained

2 ✪ Read the text again. Tick (✓) the correct box.

The text is about … .

a memory competitions ☐

b where animals hide their food ☐

c human and animal memories ☐

3 ✪✪ Complete the sentences with the words below.

> birds   chimpanzees   lists   memory   scientists

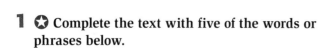

1 Scientists tested chimpanzees and humans.
2 The .... did better in the numbers test.
3 Clark's Nutcrackers have got a very good ....
4 The .... found their seeds.
5 People write .... to remember things.

4 ✪✪ Read the text again. Write *true* or *false*. Correct the false sentences.

1 In the test on the chimpanzees, there were numbers on a computer screen which then disappeared. ....
2 The chimpanzees could remember where the numbers were. ....
3 The Clark's Nutcracker birds hid over 20 seeds in an area of about 1000 square kms. ....
4 The birds returned to look for the seeds after six months. ....
5 In the scientists' experiments, humans used different techniques to animals to memorise objects. ....
6 Animals can train their brains. ....

5 ✪✪✪ Answer the questions.

1 How did the humans train their brains to memorise objects in the memory experiments?
....
....

2 'Who's got the best memory: humans or animals?' Why is this a difficult question to answer?
....
....

3 Do you have a good memory?
....
....

4 What memory techniques do you use?
....
....

Vocabulary

Adjectives: feelings

1 ✪ **Choose the correct words.**

I remember my first day at school. I was very happy and ¹**excited** / **bored** that morning. I loved the idea of school. I walked into the classroom and saw 40 other students there – I was ²**amused** / **amazed**! But then I felt ³**confused** / **satisfied** because I couldn't find my desk. I finally found it, but I was ⁴**surprised** / **embarrassed** because I was the last person in the class to sit down. After that, my first school day was wonderful. The lessons were interesting, so I never felt ⁵**bored** / **amazed**. I was ⁶**surprised** / **embarrassed** when school ended at 3 o'clock – the day was over so quickly! The teacher was ⁷**disappointed** / **amused** and smiled when I asked her for homework. 'Not on your first day,' she said. My first day at school was great! My brother didn't like school, so he was ⁸**excited** / **annoyed** with me.

| **VOCABULARY BUILDER** | **-ed and -ing adjectives** |

3 ✪✪ **Complete the conversations with the -ed or -ing form of the words below.**

~~amaze~~   annoy   bore   confuse   disappoint   surprise

1 **A** Marian's grandfather is 110 years old.
   B That's ¹ _amazing_ .

2 **A** I got a low mark on my exam.
   B That's ² _____ .

3 **A** Yusuf is usually late, but he was early today.
   B Wow, I'm ³ _____ !

4 **A** Do you understand the instructions?
   B No, they're ⁴ _____ .

5 **A** Is that a good book?
   B No, it isn't. It's really ⁵ _____ .

6 **A** I feel really ⁶ _____ .
   B Why?
   A My brother ate my last biscuit!

2 ✪✪ **Complete the sentences with adjectives from exercise 1.**

1 Kate is late for school. How does she feel?
   She's _embarrassed_ .

2 Nasir loves football. How does he feel about going to a match today?
   He's _____ .

3 Lana worked hard on her homework. She got a good mark. How does she feel?
   She's _____ .

4 The film was long and wasn't very interesting. How did Abdullah feel?
   He was _____ .

5 Tom said, 'Turn left! No, turn right! No, turn left!' How does Tom feel?
   He's _____ .

6 How does Lisa feel when someone tells a good joke?
   She's _____ .

7 Emma is studying. Her sister is very noisy. How does Emma feel?
   She's _____ .

8 Kevin really wanted to win the swimming race, but he didn't – he came third. How did he feel?
   He was _____ .

4 ✪✪✪ **Answer the questions.**

1 What makes you feel annoyed?
   _____

2 When do you feel bored?
   _____

3 What makes you feel confused?
   _____

was, were

1 ⭐ **Choose the correct words.**

1 I (**was**)/ **were** tired last night.
2 The men **was** / **were** angry.
3 The book **didn't was** / **wasn't** boring.
4 **A** **Was** / **Were** the film interesting?
  B No, it **not** / **wasn't**.
5 Where **were you** / **you was** born?
6 **A** **Was** / **Were** the girls nervous?
  B No, they **weren't** / **wasn't**.
7 **Who was** / **When was** your favourite teacher?

2 ✪✪ **Complete the text with** *was, were, wasn't*
or *weren't*.

Sir Isaac Newton
(1642–1727)
Father: Isaac Newton, farmer (1606–1642)
Mother: Hannah Newton, housewife (1623–1679)
Education: The King's School, Grantham
            University of Cambridge

Sir Isaac Newton ¹ was an English scientist. He
² .... born in 1642, three months
after his father died. His parents ³ ....
scientists. His father, also called Isaac,
⁴ .... a successful farmer and his
mother ⁵ .... a housewife. Young Isaac
⁶ .... interested in farming – he hated
it. At university, he discovered his real interests
⁷ .... in mathematics, optics, physics
and astronomy. At first, he ⁸ ....
an excellent student at Cambridge University,
but he studied hard at home and later became
a professor there. Newton wrote many great
books. They ⁹ .... very important to
science. He wrote his most famous book, *Principia
Mathematica*, during 1685 and 1686, but it
¹⁰ .... published until 1687. He became
a very famous and important person. He died
in 1727.

3 ✪✪ **Rewrite the sentences in the past form.**

1 Karen is my best friend.
  Karen was my best friend.
2 That film is really exciting.
  ....
3 My brother's homework isn't confusing.
  ....
4 I'm not amused by Basma's jokes.
  ....
5 Are Ed and Aziz friends?
  ....

4 ✪✪ **Write questions for the answers.**

1 **A** Was Saad at school?
  B Yes, Saad was at school.
2 **A** .... ?
  B Yes, his mother and father were doctors.
3 **A** .... ?
  B Tim's brother was called Dave.
4 **A** .... ?
  B No, Jenna wasn't late this morning.
5 **A** .... ?
  B Yes, they were good at tennis.
6 **A** .... ?
  B That was Tina's teacher, Mrs Jones.

5 ✪✪✪ **Your friend lost her bag and shoes**
yesterday. Use the photos and the information in
brackets to make questions and answers.

black school bag	white shoes
£30	size 42

1 **A** Was the bag small?   (bag small)
  B No, it wasn't. It was big.
2 **A** .... ? (bag white)
  B ....
3 **A** .... ? (bag new)
  B ....
4 **A** .... ? (shoes size 40)
  B ....
5 **A** .... ? (shoes white)
  B ....
6 **A** .... ? (shoes new)
  B ....

Vocabulary

Milestones

1 ⭐ **Look at the pictures of Nasir's life. Match the phrases 1–12 with the pictures A–L.**

1 leave school .... D
2 learn to drive ....
3 be born ....
4 start a company ....
5 go to school ....
6 get a job ....
7 buy a house ....
8 graduate from university ....
9 get married ....
10 become rich ....
11 move to another country ....
12 have a child ....

A	1974	B	1979
C	1991	D	1992
E	1995	F	1996
G	1997	H	1998
I	1999	J	2004
K	2009	L	2014

2 ✪✪ **Make a timeline about Nasir's life. Use the present simple.**

1974: Nasir is born.
1979: ....
1991: ....
1992: ....
1995: ....
1996: ....
1997: ....
1998: ....
1999: ....
2004: ....
2009: ....
2014: ....

3 ✪✪ **Complete the conversations with the words below.**

born   child   company   country   ~~drive~~   get   go
house   married   rich   school   university

1 **A** When did your grandfather learn to ¹ drive ?
  B When he was 18, in 1970. That was the year my father was ² ....

2 **A** Where did your mother ³ .... to school?
  B In Scotland. She stayed there until she left ⁴ .... in 1973.

3 **A** Did your father ⁵ .... a job after he graduated from ⁶ .... ?
  B Yes, but before that he moved to another ⁷ .... – Lebanon.

4 **A** When did your parents buy their first ⁸ .... ?
  B In 1995, after they got ⁹ ....

5 **A** Did your parents become ¹⁰ .... after they started a ¹¹ .... ?
  B No, they didn't, but they had a ¹² .... Me!

4 ✪✪✪ **At what age do people usually do things in your country? Write sentences.**

1 In my country, children usually first go to school at the age of five.
  (go to school)

2 ....
  (leave school)

3 ....
  (learn to drive)

4 ....
  (graduate from university)

Past simple

1 ✪ **Complete the chart with the past simple form of the verbs.**

regular	
graduate	¹ graduated
live	2
move	3
start	4
watch	5
irregular	
be	6
become	7
do	8
go	9
have	10
learn	11
leave	12

2 ✪✪ **Complete the text with the past simple form of the verbs below.**

~~be~~ become graduate learn
leave move start watch

The story of a young doctor

Iqbal Al Assaad ¹ was born in Lebanon.
When she was only two or three years old, she
² .... her older siblings when they
studied. Then she ³ .... doing
some maths. Her family were amazed. She
⁴ .... high school when she was only
12 years old and she ⁵ .... to drive
when she was 13. After that, she ⁶ ....
to Qatar for university. She ⁷ .... when
she was 20 and ⁸ .... a doctor. Now she
works as a doctor.

3 ✪✪ **Look at the text in exercise 2 again. Complete the answers to the questions.**

1 Where was Iqbal born?
   She was born in Lebanon.
2 Did she have any siblings?
   Yes, she ....
3 When did she leave high school?
   She ....
4 When did she learn to drive?
   She ....
5 Did she go to university in Lebanon?
   No, she .... , she
   ....
6 What did she graduate as?
   She ....

4 ✪✪✪ **Write questions about Florence Nightingale, a famous English nurse. Then write the answers. Use the information below.**

1 born 1820
2 not go to school
3 become a nurse (aged 31)
4 not stay in England
5 go to Turkey
6 go to Turkey to help soldiers

1 When was she born?
   She was born in 1820.
2 Did .... ?
   ....
3 What .... ?
   ....
4 Did .... ?
   ....
5 Where .... ?
   ....
6 Why .... ?
   ....

5 ✪✪✪ **Answer the questions about yourself.**

1 Where were you born?
   ....
2 When did you start school?
   ....
3 Where were your parents born?
   ....
4 Where did they go to school?
   ....

Writing

A description of a past event

LANGUAGE FOCUS | *there was, there were*

1 ✪ **Choose the correct words.**

Hi Amy!

We had a brilliant time in London yesterday. I went there with Mum and Tina on the train. There ¹**was** /(**were**) good restaurants and ²**was** / **there was** a lot to see. ³**It** / **There** was great!

First, we went to Shakespeare's Globe Theatre. There ⁴**was** / **were** a tour with a guide. ⁵**Were there** / **There were** lots of small children on the tour and ⁶**they** / **there** were really noisy! After that, we went shopping on Oxford Street. There ⁷**was** / **were** some fantastic clothes. I got a new pair of jeans.

What did you do yesterday?

From,

Ann

2 ✪✪ **Match the questions 1–6 with the answers a–f.**

1 How many people were there?
2 Was the film good?
3 Was there any food?
4 Were there many people?
5 Were your friends at the restaurant?
6 Was there a football match on TV?

a No, there wasn't, but we had lunch later.
b Yes, it was really interesting.
c No, they weren't. It was really boring!
d Yes, there was. We watched Brazil against Italy.
e No, there weren't. There were only three people.
f There were about 30, I think.

TASK | **Description of a past event**

3 ✪✪ **Complete the email using the past simple form of the verbs in brackets.**

play (football, video games, tennis)
go (shopping, camping, to a restaurant)
buy (new jeans, DVDs, a mobile phone)
see / watch (a film, a football match, a play)

4 ✪✪✪ **Write an email to a friend about a good day or weekend.**

- Use the words below or your own ideas.
- Include linking words in your email, e.g. *After that, ... ; Finally, ...*
- Write 75–100 words.

Hi Mike,

I visited my friend in Sheffield last Saturday. First, there ¹ ..was.. (be) a football match at his school in the morning. There ² .... (be) lots of people there, and the match was very exciting. His team ³ .... (win) 3–1. Then, his father ⁴ .... (drive) us to Silverstone Racing Circuit. There wasn't a race, but we ⁵ .... (have) lunch in a café there. After that, we ⁶ .... (play) video games at his house. Later, we ⁷ .... (go) out to watch a film. Finally, I ⁸ .... (return) home in the evening.

It was a great day!

Phil

Review Unit 5 in the Student's Book and complete the exercises below. Think about your progress and choose one of the faces.

READING) Masters of memory

1 Read the text on page 47 of the Student's Book again. Answer the questions.

1 What were Stephen Wiltshire, Mahavir Jain and Dominic O'Brien all good at?

....

2 What do these numbers refer to in the text?
- 80,000 ....
- 100,000 ....
- 2808 ....

3 What are you good at remembering, e.g. numbers, pictures, words, songs?

....

....

I can understand a text about people with good memories.

VOCABULARY

2 Circle the odd one out. Then use the circled word in a sentence.

1 amazed   satisfied   disappointed

....

2 boring   not interesting   exciting

....

3 amused   surprised   boring

....

4 confused   embarrassed   memory

....

I can describe feelings.

3 Match the two halves of the phrases. Then answer the question.

1	get	**a**	to school
2	graduate	**b**	born
3	be	**c**	a house
4	buy	**d**	from university
5	get a	**e**	married
6	go	**f**	a child
7	have	**g**	job

Write about a milestone in your life or your mother or father's life. When did it happen?

....

I can talk about important life events.

GRAMMAR

4 Complete the conversation with *was*, *were*, *wasn't* or *weren't*.

Mohammed

Fatima and Laila

A ¹ .... Mohammed at home yesterday?

B No, he ² .... He ³ .... in the library.

A Why ⁴ .... he in the library?

B He had a lot of homework!

A What about Fatima and Laila? Where ⁵ .... they?

B They ⁶ .... at the library. They ⁷ .... at the shops!

I can talk about past events.

5 Choose the correct words to complete each question. Then answer the questions. Use the information in brackets.

1 A When **did** / **were** Sarah start school?
   B She .... (1986)
2 A Where did Kevin's grandparents **went** / **go** to university?
   B They .... (Cairo)
3 A **When** / **Was** did Nadia learn to drive?
   B She .... (1968)
4 A What did Mike's parents **do** / **does** in 1999?
   B They .... (buy a house)

I can talk about past events.

SPEAKING

6 Answer the questions.

1 What did you do at the weekend?

....

2 When did you last watch TV?

....

3 When did you last eat in a fast food restaurant?

....

I can talk about my weekend.

1 *Kidnapped* is set in Scotland. Match the Scottish words 1–3 with the definitions a–c. Then read the extract and check.

1 lad   **a** you
2 ye   **b** yes
3 aye   **c** boy

2 Read the extract again and answer the questions. The story is narrated by the main character, David. David is a young man who has been kidnapped by his uncle.

1 Why couldn't David see where he was when he first woke up?

2 Who did he think had organised his kidnap?

3 Why did Mr Riach take Captain Hoseason to see David?

4 What would happen if they didn't move David?

5 Where did they move David to?

3 Answer the questions. Look at the text, and use your own words and ideas.

1 Why do you think David couldn't move his hands or feet?

2 When do you think he got the cut on his head?

3 What qualities did Mr Riach possess?

4 What do you think the captain was going to do with David?

4 The ship was sailing near some Scottish islands when a huge wave knocked David and some of the sailors into the sea. Write a short paragraph about what you think happened to David.

When I woke up in darkness, my head was hurting badly, and I was unable to move my hands or feet. I could hear the sailors' shouts and the sound of the wind and the waves. The whole world seemed to go up, up, up, and then down again. I felt very ill, and at first could not understand what was happening. After a while I realised that I must be somewhere inside the ship, which was moving very fast through the water. 'I've been kidnapped!' I thought angrily. It was clear that my uncle and the captain had planned it together. I began to feel frightened and hopeless, as I lay there in the dark.

Some hours later, a light shone in my face. Mr Riach, one of the ship's officers, stood looking down at me. He washed the cut on my head, gave me some water, and told me kindly to go to sleep. The next time he came, I was feeling very hot and ill. He had brought Captain Hoseason with him.

'Now, sir, see for yourself,' said Mr Riach. 'The lad's seriously ill. We must take him out of this unhealthy hole at once.'

'That's none of your business,' answered the captain. 'Ye're paid to do your job, not worry about the boy. He's staying down here.'

'I'm only paid to be an officer on this ship,' replied Mr Riach sharply. He looked hard at the captain. 'I'm not paid, like you, to kidnap and murder –'

Hoseason turned on him angrily. 'What did ye say?' he cried. 'What do ye mean?'

'You understand,' said Mr Riach, looking calmly at him.

'You should know me by know, Mr Riach. I'm a hard man. But if ye say the lad will die –'

'Aye, he will!' said Mr Riach.

'Well, sir, put him where ye like!'

So I was carried up into the sunlight a few minutes later, and put in a cabin where some of the sailors were sleeping. It was a wonderful feeling to see the daylight and to be able to talk to people again. I lay in the cabin for several days, and after a while began to feel better.

From *Kidnapped*, Oxford Bookworms. Retold by Diane Mowat.

45

6 Risk

An incredible trip

A In 2007, actor Ewan McGregor and his ¹ stunt artist friend, Charley Boorman, began a ² _____ trip from Scotland to South Africa by motorbike. They started in the village of John O' Groats in May and drove through 18 countries to arrive in the city of Cape Town in August. They made a TV programme called *Long Way Down* with their cameraman, Claudio.

B First, Ewan and Charley drove from Scotland to France. Then they went across France, through the mountains and crossed the ³ _____ into Italy. From there, they sailed across the sea to Africa and their adventures really began!

C In Libya, they drove across the desert and there was a terrible sandstorm. In Kenya, they carried their motorbikes over a big river.

D But the most dangerous situation was in South Africa. Charley was performing stunts on his motorbike for some spectators when he hit Claudio, the cameraman. Claudio was filming on his motorbike at the time. He fell off into the road. At first he didn't move, but then he stood up. The accident really hurt Claudio, but he was very brave and continued working.

E When Ewan and Charley arrived in Cape Town, they were greeted like ⁴ _____ . Thousands of spectators and tourists were cheering for them. It was an incredible trip, but they arrived safely.

1 ✪ **Complete the article with four of the words or phrases below.**

> barrel   border   daring   fine heroes
> prohibited   ~~stunt artist~~   tightrope

2 ✪✪ **Read the article again. Match the headings 1–5 with the paragraphs A–E.**

1 A dangerous incident   D
2 A happy ending
3 Driving and sailing
4 Two continents by motorbike
5 Adventures in Africa

3 ✪✪✪ **Complete the sentences with words from the article.**

1 Ewan and Charley started their trip in the village of John O'Groats .
2 They made the trip on _____ .
3 Claudio was the _____ on the trip.
4 They went through the _____ between France and Italy.
5 They carried their bikes over a river in _____ .
6 In South Africa, Charley and Claudio had an _____ .
7 Their trip ended in the city of _____ .

4 ✪✪✪ **Answer the questions.**

1 When did Ewan and Charley start their trip?
  They started their trip in May.
2 When did they finish their trip?

3 Where did they go after France?

4 Where did Ewan and Charley see a sandstorm?

5 Where did Claudio fall off his motorbike?

6 Who greeted Ewan and Charley in Cape Town?

5 ✪✪✪ **Answer the questions.**

1 Would you like to watch *Long Way Down*? Why / Why not?

2 Do you admire Ewan and Charley? Why / Why not?

3 Would you like to make a long trip, like Ewan and Charley, when you're older?

Vocabulary

Movement

1 ✪ Match the sentence halves.

1 Felix Baumgartner fell   c
2 Chris Bromham jumped   ....
3 Takao Arayama climbed   ....
4 Chad Hundeby swam   ....
5 Michael Johnson ran   ....
6 Oliver Favre dived   ....

a up Mount Everest when he was 70 years old.
b over 18 big, red buses on his motorbike.
c through the air for 39 kms in the world's highest skydive.
d off a 53.9 metre high diving board into water.
e across the sea from England to France in seven hours and 17 minutes.
f around a 400-metre track in 43.18 seconds.

2 ✪✪ Choose the correct words.

1 I always cycle slowly so I don't fall **down** / **(off)**/ **through** my bike.
2 At the moment they're driving **off** / **along** / **across** Europe.
3 She's very good at winter sports. She can ski **down** / **under** / **up** that mountain in three minutes.
4 Tom climbed **under** / **up** / **across** the tree to get an apple.
5 Last year, Nadia jumped **up** / **out of** / **around** a plane at 1000 metres.
6 In July, we cycled **under** / **through** / **off** the mountains in Italy.

3 ✪✪ Complete the sentences with the words below.

climb down   ~~cycle through~~   fall off
run into   sail around   swim across

1 For their next holiday they want to cycle through north Germany.
2 Be careful! Don't .... that chair and hurt yourself.
3 It's impossible to .... the Atlantic!
4 I love the sea. I'd like to buy a boat and .... the world when I'm older.
5 We need to .... the mountain now because it's getting dark.
6 It's very hot today! Let's .... the sea and cool down!

VOCABULARY BUILDER | Homophones

4 ✪✪ Tick (✓) the correct words. Correct the mistakes.

Ironman Triathlon
Last year, I was in a race called 'Ironman Triathlon'. I swam 3.86 km, [1]rode my bike 108.25 km and ran 42.2 km. It wasn't easy!
In the year before the race, I [2]new I had to prepare. Every week, I went running on the [3]rodes near my house, swam in the [4]see and [5]practised cycling often. I [6]road 100 km every Sunday. I also [7]ate healthy foods – no fat, low sugar. It's very important for athletes to eat the [8]write foods. But finishing the race was the best day of my life!

1 ✓ ....   5 ....
2 ....   6 ....
3 ....   7 ....
4 ....   8 ....

5 ✪✪✪ What would you like to do when you're older? Write sentences using prepositions and the places below, or your own ideas.

Africa   a plane   a waterfall   Mount Everest
Mount Fuji   the Red Sea   the Sahara Desert   the US

1 ....
2 ....
3 ....

Past continuous: positive and negative

1 ✪ Choose the correct words.

Baumgartner's daring descent

On 14th October 2012, stunt artist Felix Baumgartner jumped out of a balloon 39 kilometres above the Earth. As he ¹ **was** / **were** falling, he reached a speed of 1358 kilometres per hour.

While he ² **was** / **were** preparing for his big jump, Baumgartner made two smaller jumps. The first was from 21,800 metres and the second was from 29,400 metres. Helpers on the ground ³ **was** / **were** watching the jumps carefully and they ⁴ **was** / **were** using computers to check Baumgartner's health as he fell.

Baumgartner and his team ⁵ **was** / **were** originally planning the big jump for 5th October, but it was windy and they ⁶ **was** / **were** having problems with the radio. They tried again on 11th October, but again the wind ⁷ **was** / **were** blowing and the mission was stopped. Finally, on 14th October, as 8 million people ⁸ **was** / **were** watching on the internet, Baumgartner safely made the 11-minute journey from the edge of space back to Earth.

2 ✪✪ Complete the sentences with *was*, *were*, *wasn't* or *weren't*.

1 They ___were___ having dinner at 8 o'clock last night.
2 In this photo we _____ visiting Dubai.
3 Mohammed _____ reading a magazine in class. He was studying.
4 Look at this holiday video of my sister. She _____ swimming in Croatia.
5 You _____ listening to the teacher. You were looking at your mobile phone.
6 I _____ wearing a sweater yesterday because it was very hot.
7 We _____ cycling through Poland in June. I remember it well.
8 We _____ driving through the Czech Republic three hours ago. We were still at home.

3 ✪✪ Write complete answers to the questions. Use the words in brackets.

1 What were you doing at 12 o'clock yesterday? (walk through the park)
   I was walking through the park at 12 o'clock yesterday.
2 What was Cathy doing an hour ago? (play tennis)
   _____
3 What were they doing at 7 o'clock yesterday evening? (climb a mountain)
   _____
4 What was she doing at 9 o'clock last Saturday? (not ski)
   _____
5 What was the weather like yesterday afternoon? (not rain)
   _____
6 What were you doing last Sunday morning? (sail)
   _____

4 ✪✪ Complete the text with the past continuous form of the verbs below.

| cycle | have | not do | not listen |
| not study | relax | sail | watch |

Last week my friends and I ¹ _weren't studying_ at school and we ² _____ to our teacher. We ³ _____ fun on an adventure holiday! Kevin and Jamal ⁴ _____ down a mountain on their bikes, and I ⁵ _____ across a lake. But my twin sister Nadia ⁶ _____ exciting things. She ⁷ _____ in her room at the hotel with her friends and they ⁸ _____ TV!

5 ✪✪✪ Write about a day last week. Write a positive and a negative sentence for each time.

7.00 a.m.: _I wasn't sleeping at 7.00 a.m._
I was having a shower.

11.00 a.m.: _____

1.00 p.m.: _____

4.00 p.m.: _____

8.00 p.m.: _____

Extreme sports

1 ⭐ **Match the words below with the pictures.**

> bungee jumping   cave diving   hang-gliding
> ice climbing   kitesurfing   sandboarding
> white-water rafting   ~~wingsuit flying~~

1   wingsuit flying

2   ....

3   ....

4   ....

5   ....

6   ....

7   ....

8   ....

2 ⭐⭐ **Complete the conversations with the words from exercise 1.**

A   Where do you go [1] _hang-gliding_ ?

B   We jump off a mountain and land in a field.

A   Do you jump out of a plane when you do [2] .... ?

B   Yes. It's a lot like skydiving.

A   Where did you go [3] .... ?

B   I jumped off a bridge in New Zealand.

A   Do you have to be a good swimmer to go [4] .... ?

B   Yes, you do. You often fall into the sea.

A   Did you go [5] .... on your holiday?

B   Yes! I fell out of the boat!

A   What's [6] .... like?

B   It's like snowboarding, but you do it in the desert.

A   Where can you do [7] .... ?

B   You can go up frozen waterfalls.

A   Would you like to try [8] .... ?

B   No! I can't stand swimming underwater!

3 ⭐⭐ **Complete the blog post with four of the extreme sports from exercise 1.**

🖵🖴✖

My blog post: extreme sports

I'm interested in trying some new extreme sports. I learnt scuba diving on holiday in Malaysia, so I think [1] _cave diving_ would be fun. In winter, I sometimes go snowboarding. In summer, next time I'm near a desert, I want to try [2] ....

There are some extreme sports that I wouldn't like to try, though. I don't like flying, so I don't want to try [3] .... Also, I don't like very high places, so I think [4] .... would be too scary for me.

4 ⭐⭐⭐ **Write a blog post about one extreme sport that you would like to try and one that you wouldn't like to try.**

Past continuous: questions

1 ⭐ **Complete the conversations with *was*, *were*, *wasn't* or *weren't*.**

A ¹ _Was_ Lana sleeping?
B Yes, she ² _____ .
A ³ _____ Mum and Dad climbing?
B No, they ⁴ _____ .
A What ⁵ _____ Hassan reading?
B He ⁶ _____ reading a comic.
A Where ⁷ _____ you going?
B We ⁸ _____ going to school.
A ⁹ _____ it raining yesterday?
B No, it ¹⁰ _____ .

2 ⭐⭐ **Write questions for the answers using the past continuous. Use the verbs in brackets.**

1 _Where was she going?_ (go)
  She was going to the London marathon.
2 _____ ? (rain)
  Yes, it was. I got really wet!
3 _____ ? (talk)
  She was talking to her best friend.
4 _____ ? (do)
  She was sandboarding in the desert.
5 _____ ? (feel)
  I was feeling very nervous.
6 _____ ? (backpack)
  They were backpacking around Canada.

3 ⭐⭐⭐ **Write six questions about Mike's day using the past continuous. Then write the answers for Mike.**

1 **Question:** _Were you sleeping at 6.30 a.m.?_
  Mike: _No, I wasn't. I was eating breakfast._
2 **Question:** _____
  Mike: _____
3 **Question:** _____
  Mike: _____
4 **Question:** _____
  Mike: _____
5 **Question:** _____
  Mike: _____
6 **Question:** _____
  Mike: _____

Past simple and past continuous

4 ⭐⭐ **Complete the sentences using the past simple or past continuous form of the verbs in brackets.**

1 I _was climbing_ up the mountain when I _found_ a camera. (climb / find)
2 They _____ across the river when the boat _____ . (swim / arrive)
3 Maya _____ a bad accident while she _____ down a mountain in the Alps. (have / ski)
4 _____ Faisal _____ when the teacher _____ him a question? (listen / ask)
5 We _____ at the Great Wall when we _____ through China. (stop / travel)
6 _____ you _____ when the storm _____ ? (drive / start)

5 ⭐⭐⭐ **Write sentences about a holiday or a day out. Use the past simple and the past continuous.**

1 _____
_____
2 _____
_____
3 _____
_____

MIKE'S DAY

midnight–6.00 a.m.	sleep
6.00 a.m.–6.30 a.m.	eat breakfast
6.30 a.m.–7.30 a.m.	drive to the beach
7.30 a.m.–midday	kitesurf on the beach
midday–1.00 p.m.	eat lunch
1.00 p.m.–5.00 p.m.	kitesurf on the beach
5.00 p.m.–6.00 p.m.	drive home
6.00 p.m.–7.00 p.m.	eat dinner
7.00 p.m.–9.30 p.m.	watch a film
9.30 p.m.–midnight	sleep

Writing

A narrative text

1 ✪ **Choose the correct words.**

1 He saw a big fish **as soon as** / (**while**) he was swimming across the lake.
2 My dad was waiting for me at the station **when** / **while** I arrived.
3 I kissed my grandmother **as soon as** / **while** she opened the door.
4 We were standing at the bus stop **when** / **while** it started to rain.
5 Jack fell over **as soon as** / **while** he was playing football.
6 I just saw a terrible car accident! Phone the police **as soon as** / **when** you can!
7 **While** / **As soon as** we were exploring the mountain, we saw a bear!

2 ✪✪ **Complete the sentences with *when, while* or *as soon as*.**

1 I was running to school ..when... I met my friend.
2 He left the house .... you were talking on the phone.
3 He was very sad .... his dog died.
4 They were playing tennis .... they lost the ball.
5 We took some photos of tigers .... we were travelling through India.
6 She phoned the police .... she saw the boy fall through the ice.

3 ✪✪ **Read the story. Number the paragraphs in the correct order 1–5.**

.... On Saturday, I was sailing in a small boat with my friend Sarah when she suddenly stood up. The boat moved and I fell into the sea. It was very cold!

.... Then I ran up the beach to our hotel and I put on some dry clothes. I felt much better after that, but I was upset about the camera.

..1.. I remember when I went to the Isle of Wight with my class for the weekend. We were learning to sail with an instructor called Tim.

.... As soon as Tim saw me, he came to rescue me.

.... I was lucky because he was very near the boat when the accident happened. But while he was helping me, I dropped my camera into the water and I lost all my photos!

4 ✪✪✪ **Write a story. Use the text in exercise 3 as a model.**

- Use the information in these notes:
- Write 100–150 words.

Trip to: the French Alps with class for one week
Learning to: ski
Instructor: Suzy
Problem 1: yesterday / ski down mountain / fall over
Rescue: as soon as / Suzy / see me / ski over to me
Problem 2: while / help me / fall over again / break new sunglasses
Later: go to café / feel better / upset about sunglasses

6 | Self-evaluation

Review Unit 6 in the Student's Book and complete the exercises below. Think about your progress and choose one of the faces.

READING ▶ Niagara Falls – Don't look down!

1 Read the text on page 55 of the Student's Book again. Answer the questions.

1 What did Blondin, The Great Signor Farini and Annie Taylor all do?

_____

2 What do these numbers refer to?
- 50: _____
- 2.5 million: _____
- 1859: _____
- 1860: _____

3 Do you think the $10,000 fine is a good or bad idea? Why?

_____

> I can understand a text about the history of a famous place.

VOCABULARY

2 Choose the correct words.

1 Let's climb **down** / **under** the mountain now.
2 It was hot, so we ran **into** / **up** the sea.
3 Mohammed and Yusuf are cycling **off** / **through** the mountains this week.
4 I want to sail **around** / **under** the world.
5 Did Karen fall **down** / **off** her bike?
6 Asma is swimming **under** / **across** the lake.

> I can talk about daring stunts.

3 Circle the odd one out. Explain each choice.

1 ice climbing   wingsuit flying   sandboarding

_____

2 bungee jumping   cave diving   white-water rafting

_____

3 wingsuit flying   hang-gliding   ice climbing

_____

4 white-water rafting   kitesurfing   sandboarding

_____

> I can describe some extreme sports.

GRAMMAR

4 Choose the correct words. Then answer the questions.

1 What **you were** / **were you** doing at 8 o'clock yesterday morning?

_____

2 **Was** / **Did** the sun shining yesterday?

_____

3 Were you **having** / **have** breakfast at 5 o'clock this morning?

_____

4 How were you **feeling** / **felt** before your last exam?

_____

> I can say what was happening at a past event.

5 Complete the sentences with the past simple or past continuous form of the verbs in brackets.

A I ¹_____ (see) something amazing yesterday! I ²_____ (walk) through town when I looked up and there was a man with a parachute jumping off a building!

B That is amazing! What ³_____ he _____ (do)?

A He was a BASE jumper, and he and his team ⁴_____ (make) a film.

B ⁵_____ (be) the police there?

A Yes, they ⁶_____ (be). They ⁷_____ (stop) cars from driving along the road below the building. They ⁸_____ (want) him to land safely.

B That's really interesting.

> I can talk about interrupted actions in the past.

SPEAKING

6 Correct the mistake in each phrase.

1 I'm not believe it! _____
2 Wow! That's amazed! _____
3 Real? _____
4 It's kidding! _____
5 Good done! _____

> I can express interest.

1 Match the paragraphs 1–3 with the photos A–C in the advertisement.

Visitors Love Turkey!

1 'Going down the river was great. The weather was very hot, so when we fell into the water, it was nice. While we were having lunch, our guides explained a lot about nature: the plants and animals around us. It was wonderful.'

2 'As we entered the water, I was feeling nervous. The dive was beautiful. The cave was big, and we could see the sky through a hole in the top. While we were diving, I was so happy and relaxed. It was beautiful!'

3 'When I was at the top, looking down, I was very afraid. But then we counted 3, 2, 1 and I was falling through the air! It was an amazing experience. I did it three times!'

2 Make an advertisement that shows three extreme sports in your country. Follow the steps in the project checklist.

- Choose three extreme sports that can be done in your country.
- Find and draw pictures of each sport.
- Write about peoples' experiences doing the sports.
- Make an advertisement. Write the peoples' experiences next to the pictures.

TALK ABOUT IT

3 Exchange your advertisement with your classmates. How are they similar? How are they different?

Amber and I both chose sandboarding for our advertisements.

Samir's advertisment is for extreme sports in the air, but mine is for extreme sports in the water.

Learning at home

In the UK, some families feel that learning at home is better than going to school. Home-schooled children, or their families, can choose what to learn and when.

Adam is 13 years old. He has a high ¹ IQ and is an excellent student of maths. He could do difficult maths problems when he was only five years old. He can also speak French, German and Japanese ² .... – and English, of course. He wants to start university by the age of 15. Sometimes his parents ³ .... him to slow down and enjoy life, but he is very hard-working. He found school lessons much easier than most children, but making friends was more difficult. At home he can spend more time on his favourite subjects and he is preparing to take many of his exams early. Does he ever take a break? 'Yes,' he says. 'I'm ⁴ .... about maths and languages, but I don't study subjects I'm not interested in.'

Tina is also 13 years old. Her parents weren't happy with the local school, so they made a decision to teach her at home. Her favourite subject is history and she often goes to museums to study. 'I couldn't do that before, when I was at school,' she says. Her parents don't ⁵ .... her very hard, but they're always happy to help and they're ⁶ .... about Tina's studying hours – she studies every day, but not at the weekend.

Adam and Tina love learning at home, but some people think that studying at school is more useful because it trains you for adult life. It teaches you to be with people you don't always like, but it can also help you to make friends. Are these things more important than lessons? What do you think?

1 ✪ **Complete the text with six of the words below.**

> ambitious encourage fluently genius
> ~~IQ~~ push strict talented

2 ✪ **Read the text again. Tick (✓) the correct box.**

The writer of the text …

a thinks that home-schooling is a bad idea. ☐

b thinks that home-schooling is better for everyone. ☐

c doesn't say if home-schooling is good or bad and asks the reader to decide. ☐

3 ✪✪ **Complete the sentences with the words below.**

> learns likes maths parents
> ~~school~~ subject university

1 In the UK, people can learn at home or at __school__ .

2 Adam is very good at .... and languages.

3 Adam wants to start .... when he's 14 or 15.

4 He only studies things that he ....

5 History is Tina's favourite ....

6 She .... at home and in museums.

7 Tina's .... always help her when she needs it.

4 ✪ **Write *true* or *false*. Correct the false sentences.**

1 Home-schooled children study some of the same subjects as children at school. ....

2 Adam started university at 13 years old.
....

3 Adam's parents are strict and push him very hard. ....

4 Tina's parents don't push her too hard.
....

5 Tina only studies on Mondays, Tuesdays and Fridays. ....

6 Tina doesn't like studying at home. ....

5 ✪✪✪ **Answer the questions.**

1 Why do Adam's parents sometimes encourage him to slow down?

2 Why did Tina's parents start home-schooling her?

3 What are two advantages of home-schooling?

4 Do some children in your country learn at home?

5 Would you like to try home-schooling? Why / Why not?

6 Do you think home-schooling is a good idea? Why / Why not?

Skills and people

1 ⭐ **Match the words below with the pictures.**

| compose   design   invent   paint   ~~program~~   write |

1   program   2 ....

3 ....   4 ....

5 ....   6 ....

2 ✪✪ **For each skill (verb) from exercise 1, write the person (noun) who does it.**

1 programmer	4 ....
2	5 ....
3	6 ....

3 ✪✪ **Complete the paragraphs with the verbs or nouns from exercises 1 and 2.**

I play the piano and ¹ compose music. You can hear my songs on the radio, in advertisements. I work as a ² .... for a company that produces radio advertisements.

I'm a website ³ .... I ⁴ .... and create websites for local businesses. At university I studied computing. After university, I worked for a few years as a computer ⁵ .... , making video games. I still like to ⁶ .... video games, but I don't make any money from it – it's just a hobby.

I think of new ideas for products and then I ⁷ .... them. I have my own small company. I work alone and then I sell my inventions to big companies. I love being an ⁸ .... !

VOCABULARY BUILDER | **Phrases with** *by*

4 ✪✪ **Choose the correct words.**

1   **A**   Did you do the housework by ¹**heart** /(**yourself**?)
     B   No, Fahad helped me.

2   **A**   Did you plan to meet Bill yesterday?
     B   No, I met him by ²**hand** / **accident**.

3   **A**   Have you got a pen by ³**any chance** / **law**?
     B   Yes, I have. Here you are.

4   **A**   Was your hat made by ⁴**yourself** / **hand**?
     B   Yes, it was. My mother made it.

5   **A**   Can I park here?
     B   No, it's a 'no-parking' area by ⁵**law** / **accident**.

6   **A**   How was your exam?
     B   It was fine, thanks. I knew all of the answers by ⁶**chance** / **heart**.

5 ✪✪✪ **Answer the questions.**

1   Which of the jobs in exercise 2 would you most like to do when you're older? Why?

     ....

     ....

2   Which of the jobs in exercise 2 would you least like to do when you're older? Why?

     ....

     ....

can and could for ability

1 ⭐ **Choose the correct words.**

1 I **don't can** / **can't** program a computer.
2 We **can't** / **no can** cook.
3 She **didn't could** / **couldn't** swim.
4 Mohammed **can to** / **can** play tennis.
5 After the car accident, he **can't** / **couldn't** walk for six months.
6 I **can** / **could** run fast when I was younger, but not anymore. Now I run very slowly!
7 Amira can **speaks** / **speak** French fluently.
8 Jane **can** / **can't** paint. She painted a very good picture of some mountains last week.

2 ⭐⭐ **Rewrite the positive sentences in the negative form and the negative sentences in the positive form.**

1 I couldn't play the guitar when I was young.
  I could play the guitar when I was young.
2 Samira can't play tennis.

3 Yusuf could paint pictures when he was four.

4 We couldn't cook when we were children.

5 Mike and Emir can't program a computer.

6 You can speak German.

3 ⭐⭐ **Complete the sentences with the words below.**

can can't could could ~~couldn't~~

1 Christy Brown _couldn't_ move most parts of his body. He was paralysed, but he could write novels and paint pictures with his left foot.
2 Pablo Picasso was very young when he started to paint. He _____ paint from the age of seven.
3 Bruce Willis _____ play the harmonica as well as act. He plays it in his band, The Accelerators.
4 Erik Weihenmayer _____ see, but in May 2001 he climbed Mount Everest. He was the first blind person to climb the mountain.
5 A _____ Rihanna sing from a young age?
  B Yes, she could. She started singing when she was seven.

4 ⭐⭐ **Make sentences with can, can't, could or couldn't and some of the words below.**

people
I my friend my grandparents my mum / dad

verbs
cook dance drive play run sing speak swim

time expressions
in (2005) last (year) now when (I) was (young / little)

1 I couldn't drive a car when I was little.
2
3
4
5

Questions with How

5 ⭐⭐ **Look at the answers and write questions with How. Use the words in brackets.**

1 A How strict is your teacher? (teacher)
  B She's very strict.
2 A _____ ? (foreign languages)
  B I can speak two foreign languages.
3 A _____ ? (in the park)
  B They ran six km.
4 A _____ ? (sleep / last night)
  B I got eight hours of sleep.
5 A _____ ? (guitar)
  B He practises every day.
6 A _____ ? (sister)
  B She's 1.6 metres tall.

6 ⭐⭐⭐ **Complete the questions with How and the words below. Then answer the questions about yourself.**

~~far~~ many much often tall

1 How far _____ can you swim?
2 _____ people are there in your family?
3 _____ are you?
4 _____ water do you drink each day?
5 _____ do you go shopping?

1 I can swim 600 metres.
2
3
4
5

Jobs

1 ✪ **Match the jobs below with the photos 1–10.**

> an accountant   an architect   an electrician
> a fashion designer   a lawyer   a librarian
> a mechanic   ~~a nurse~~   a software developer
> a tour guide

1   a nurse

2   ....

3   ....

4   ....

5   ....

6   ....

7   ....

8   ....

9   ....

10   ....

2 ✪✪ **Complete the sentences with the jobs from exercise 1.**

1   A mechanic .... can repair machines.
2   .... tells tourists about places.
3   .... creates new styles of clothing.
4   .... works in a library and knows a lot about books.
5   .... looks after people in hospital.
6   .... knows how to program a computer.
7   .... designs buildings.
8   .... works in the legal system.
9   .... puts electrical systems in houses or repairs them.
10 .... knows a lot about money.

3 ✪✪ **Complete the advertisements with the jobs from exercises 1 and 2.**

> **¹ Electrician wanted**
>
> This is an interesting and skilled job working for a local company. You must be able to do anything, from changing a light bulb to putting large electrical systems into houses. Call Sam Davis on 609-732-867 for more information.

> **Job opportunity for an ²**...............
>
> This is a skilled job and it requires a lot of training, but it is well paid. You must be good at maths and good at dealing with money. You will need to manage our customers' accounts. Contact Bill Tomlinson on 777-596-948 to apply.

> **Job opening for a skilled ³**...............
> We are looking for a new employee at our garage in the centre of town. You must be skilled and well trained in repairing cars and vans. Call Mike on 986-547-360.

> **⁴**............... **needed**
>
> I'm looking for somebody to plan and design two new rooms for our house. We need a bigger house for our family. Can you help?
> Email salinab@qmail.com.

> **Experienced ⁵**............... **wanted**
> We're a small company looking for somebody with a very good knowledge of Istanbul. You will give visitors information about the sights of the city and talk about its fascinating history. Call Jenna on 987-489-025.

4 ✪✪✪ **Write a short job advertisement for one of the jobs below.**

> fashion designer   lawyer   librarian
> nurse   software developer

....
....
....
....

5 ✪✪✪ **Which three jobs from exercises 1 and 2 would you most like to do? Why?**

1   ....

2   ....

3   ....

should and must

1 ✪ **Choose the correct words.**

Jamal   I love computer games. I want to be a software developer. What do you think I ¹**must** / **should** study at university?

Laila   You ²**should** / **must** work hard at maths and study computer science.

Jamal   Yes, I think you're right. Er … what time is it?

Laila   Five to nine. Why?

Jamal   Oh, no! I have a maths test in five minutes! I ³**shouldn't** / **mustn't** be late!

Basma   You ⁴**shouldn't** / **mustn't** leave your bike here.

Hassan   Why not?

Basma   Look at the sign – NO BIKES. It's against the rules.

Hassan   Oh, OK. Thanks. So where do you think I ⁵**must** / **should** leave my bike?

Basma   In the bike parking area, and you ⁶**should** / **must** lock it.

2 ✪✪ **Complete the text with** *should, shouldn't, must* **or** *mustn't*.

FutureElectrician asks:

I'm 15 years old. I want to be an electrician. Sometimes I repair electrical problems at home. What ¹ should I do to start working as an electrician?

Reply

Replies:

Aziz22 says:
Be careful. You ² .... have qualifications to work as an electrician! You ³ .... make electrical repairs on your own. It's illegal!

Karen54 says:
You ⁴ .... work hard in your science classes at school. Can you find an electrician in your town? You ⁵ .... offer to help, to get experience.

Amber1 says:
You're young. You ⁶ .... choose a job now because you might not know about all your options. You ⁷ .... work hard at school and try to go to a good university. Then decide when you are older.

Phil99 says:
You ⁸ .... become an electrician! My dad is an electrician and he hates it! :-(

3 ✪✪ **Write a sentence for signs 1–8. Use** *must* **and** *mustn't*.

1. You must wash your hands.
2. ....
3. ....
4. ....
5. ....
6. ....
7. ....
8. ....

4 ✪✪✪ **Imagine a student from England is visiting your home town or city. Complete the sentences with advice for their visit.**

1. You should ....
2. You should ....

3. You shouldn't ....
4. You shouldn't ....

A biography

LANGUAGE FOCUS | Time expressions

1 ★ **Choose the correct words.**

1　Swimmer Michael Phelps was born **in** / **on** 1985.

2　TV chef Jamie Oliver worked at his parents' restaurant **during** / **for** eight years before he went to catering college.

3　Mozart was composing music **by** / **for** the age of five.

4　Ayrton Senna had his first Formula One race in 1984. Four years **late** / **later**, he was world champion.

5　Cristiano Ronaldo is **now** / **for** the highest-paid footballer in the world.

6　Bill Gates started programming computers **in** / **by** high school.

2 ★★ **Complete the sentences with the words below.**

| by for in later now ~~on~~ |

1　Nuri Şahin was born _on_ 5th September, 1988.

2　He won a prize .... 2005 at the Under-17 World Cup.

3　Şahin was a professional footballer .... the time he was 16 years old.

4　He played football in Germany and the Netherlands .... five years, from 2005 to 2010.

5　Two years .... he moved to Liverpool in the UK.

6　After playing football in many countries, he is .... fluent in five languages: Turkish, German, English, Dutch and Spanish.

TASK | A biography

3 ★★ **Complete the text using the information on the right.**

Susie Wolff

Susie Wolff was born in Oban, Scotland in 1982. She grew up and went to school there.

She was interested in ¹ _motor racing_ from the age of eight and finished fifth place in the Formula Renault UK Championship in ² .... Her life changed in 2012 when she had her ³ .... After that, she became known as 'The Fastest Woman in the World.' She has won an award from ⁴ .... for women in sport.

Susie's ⁵ .... for being the only ⁶ .... in Formula One today. In her free time, she enjoys ⁷ .... and ⁸ ....

Name: Susie Wolff

From: Scotland

Early life: interested in motor racing from age of eight

Career: 1991 first race; 2004 fifth place in Formula Renault UK Championship; 2005–2012 raced all over the world; 2012 first Formula One race; 2013 won an award for women in sport from Edinburgh University

Famous for: being the only woman in Formula One today

Hobbies: skiing and cycling

4 ★★★ **Write a biography of a famous person. Use the biography in exercise 3 as a model.**

- Put the information into three paragraphs:
  1　Where was the person born? Where did he / she grow up?
  2　What is the person good at or interested in? When did he / she become interested in it and how did he / she become successful at it?
  3　What is the person famous for today? What other things is he / she interested in?
- Write 100–150 words.

READING ▶ Prodigy!

1 **Read the text on page 65 of the Student's Book again. Answer the questions.**

1 What was special about Wendy Vo, S. Chandrasekhar, Ainan Cawley, János Starker and Elise Tan-Roberts?

2 What could Wendy Vo do when she was eight?

3 What was S. Chandrasekhar very good at?

4 What did Ainan Cawley's parents want him to do when he was seven?

5 Would you like to be a genius? Why / Why not?

I can understand a text about talented children.

VOCABULARY

2 **Complete the sentences. Then answer the question.**

composed   design   ~~invented~~   painted   programmed

1 Ann _invented_ a new type of chair.
2 Can you help me _____ my website?
3 Tom _____ a picture of a tree.
4 Emir _____ three songs.
5 Who _____ the first computer?

Can you describe what any of these famous people did: Mozart, Picasso, Pascal, the Brontë sisters?

I can talk about the skills of famous people.

3 **Match the two halves of the job words. Then answer the question.**

1 fashion   a guide
2 elect   b designer
3 arch   c itect
4 software   d developer
5 tour   e rician

Describe one of the jobs above. For example, is it interesting, well-paid, skilled?

I can discuss what jobs are like.

GRAMMAR

4 **Complete the sentences about yourself. Use can, can't, could or couldn't.**

1 When I was three, I _____ walk.
2 When I was five, I _____ speak English.
3 When I was five, I _____ cook.
4 When I was seven, I _____ swim.
5 I _____ ride a bike.
6 I _____ speak two languages fluently.
7 I _____ ski.

I can talk about my abilities in the present and the past.

5 **Rewrite the sentences about being a good student using should(n't) or must(n't).**

1 It's necessary to
   You _____
2 It's against the school rules to use your mobile in class.
   You _____
3 It's a bad idea to talk in class.
   You _____
4 It's a good idea to do your homework every night.
   You _____

I can give recommendations and instructions.

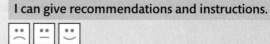

SPEAKING

6 **Answer the questions.**

1 What are you good at doing?

2 What are you bad at doing?

3 What can you definitely not do?

4 What is your friend good at doing?

5 What can your friend definitely not do?

I can talk about people's skills.

1 Look at the title of the book and the picture. Which of the words below do you think are in the extract? Read the extract quickly and check.

accident brother dream email lawyer
newspaper prison shops spy station
station master tea-time train driver waiting room

2 Read the extract again and answer the questions.

1 Why did the children stop asking questions about their father?

2 Why did Bobbie go to the station?

3 When did she first notice the story in the newspaper?

4 How did Mother know that something was wrong with Bobbie?

5 What did Bobbie do to explain what was wrong?

3 Answer the questions. Look at the extract, and use your own words and ideas.

1 Why do you think Mother and the children moved to the white house?

2 Do you think the family was rich? Why / Why not?

3 How do you think Bobbie felt when she first read the name of the spy?

4 What kind of person is Mother? What is her personality?

4 *The Railway Children* has a happy ending. Write a short paragraph about what you think happens at the end of the story.

When the children first went to live at the white house, they talked about Father a lot and were always asking questions about him. But as time passed, their questions seemed to make Mother unhappy, so they stopped asking them. But they never forgot him.

Bobbie thought about Father often. She knew her mother was unhappy, and she worried a lot about that. And why was Father away for so long? Was there something that Mother wasn't telling them?

The answer came on the day she went to the station, to fetch the magazines. They were old magazines which people left on trains or in the waiting room. Perks said the children could have them to read, and one day Bobbie went to fetch them.

'I'll just put some newspaper round them to keep them together,' said Perks. And he took an old newspaper from the heap.

The magazines were heavy, and Bobbie stopped to rest on the way home. She sat on the grass and dropped them beside her. As she did this, she looked at the newspaper and read some of the words on the page … and it was like a terrible dream.

She never remembered how she got home. But she went to her room and locked the door. Then she took the newspaper off the magazines and looked at it again. The words seemed to jump out at her:
FIVE YEARS IN PRISON FOR SPY!

And the name of the 'spy' was the name of her father.

Bobbie was very quiet at tea-time.

'Is anything wrong?' Mother asked her.

'I'm all right,' said Bobbie.

But after tea, Mother went up to Bobbie's room. 'What's the matter?' she wanted to know.

For an answer, Bobbie took the newspaper from under her bed and showed it to her mother.

'Oh, Bobbie!' cried Mother. 'You don't believe it, do you? You don't believe Daddy is a spy?'

'No!' said Bobbie.

'He's good and honest and he's done nothing wrong,' said Mother. 'We have to remember that.'

8 City to city

Songdo: South Korea's Futuristic City

Like many big cities, Songdo, South Korea, has a lot of **¹ skyscrapers** . About 70,000 people live there now, but there are 80,000 flats, a lot of offices, shops and some smaller houses. There are also hotels, meeting centres for businesses and a hospital. The city won't be finished until 2016, but new people are arriving to live in Songdo every day.

Amazingly, the city produces almost no **²**_____. How is this possible? Songdo is a completely new city – the plans for the city were completed in 2003. It was designed to use only **³**_____ and built to be very **⁴**_____ . The city opened for business in 2009.

Songdo's planners, designers and architects wanted to take the best ideas for cities from around the world, and improve the worst parts. Careful planning avoids crowding and **⁵**_____ by including wide roads and lots of small parks.

In the centre of the city is Central Park, just like in New York City. It's an open, green area for relaxation and recreation. There are also canals, just like in Venice in Italy, and there are restaurants, markets, cinemas and concert halls, just like in other great cities.

People can cycle everywhere in the city and enjoy shopping, play golf or go to a museum. Offices and flats are very close together, so walking to work is easy. Of course there are schools, too.

With all of these qualities, Songdo is called a 'smart city'. Many people believe that more new cities like Songdo should be built to solve the problems of pollution and housing **⁶**_____ around the world.

Come to Songdo! It's the future … now.

---

1 ✪ Complete the article with six of the words or phrases below.

> environmentally friendly   migrate
> overpopulation   pollution   renewable energy
> shortages   ~~skyscrapers~~   trend

2 ✪ Read the article again. Tick (✓) the correct box.

The city of Songdo …

a is planned and building will start in the future. ☐

b is a new city, but it isn't finished. ☐

c is built and completed. ☐

3 ✪✪ Write *true* or *false*. Correct the false statements.

1 About 80,000 people live in Songdo. ....
2 A lot of people are moving away from Songdo.
3 Pollution isn't a big problem in Songdo.
4 Before 2009, no one lived in Songdo. ....
5 People in Songdo cycle and walk a lot. ....

4 ✪✪✪ Answer the questions.

1 Why is Songdo described as 'environmentally friendly'?
....
....

2 How does Songdo's design help to avoid crowding and overpopulation in the city?
....
....

3 What ideas did Songdo's designers take from other cities around the world? Name two.
....
....

4 Why is it easy to walk to work in Songdo?
....
....

5 What do you think is the best thing about Songdo?
....
....

6 Would you like to live in Songdo? Why / Why not?
....
....

Vocabulary

In towns and cities

1 ✪ **Match words 1–8 with the things A–H in the picture.**

1 petrol station
2 traffic lights
3 pedestrian crossing
4 ~~high-rise building~~
5 multi-storey car park
6 green space
7 main road
8 retail park

2 ✪✪ **Complete the sentences with the words from exercise 1.**

1 I need fuel for the car. Let's stop at the next _petrol station_ .

2 Cars must stop at the .... when people need to cross the road.

3 The .... goes through the town centre.

4 My father's office is on the tenth floor of a ....

5 When the .... show a green light, cars can go, but they must stop at a red light.

6 We can leave our car in the .... when we go shopping.

7 The city's got a lot of .... for walking and playing ball games.

8 There are a lot of shops in the ....

VOCABULARY BUILDER | Numbers and times

3 ✪✪ **Choose the correct words.**

Understanding time

It's difficult for people to imagine very large numbers. For example, the distance from the Earth to the Sun is about 149 [1]**million** / **millennium** / **century** kilometres. But what does that mean? Think of it this way: a car on the motorway goes about 110 kilometres [2]**a second** / **an hour** / **a week**. A car driving from the Earth to the Sun would take about 1,327,000 hours. That's the same as 151 [3]**billion** / **dozen** / **years**!

Shorter periods of time, for example [4]**an hour** / **nought** / **a half**, are easier for people. That's because we experience these every [5]**day** / **hundred** / **couple**.

An average person lives about seven [6]**quarters** / **decades** / **months**. That's 70 years – less than 1000 [7]**centuries** / **months** / **seconds**. And how long did it take you to read this text? Just a [8]**hundred** / **few** / **half** minutes!

4 ✪✪✪ **Answer the questions. Write complete sentences.**

1 How long does your journey to school take?

....

2 How many people live in your town or city?

....

3 What's the population of your country?

....

4 How old is your house or flat?

....

will / won't

1 ⭐ **Choose the correct words.**

1 **Rashid** What country ¹(will)/ wills you live in when you're older?

   Hassan I ²will / won't live abroad. I definitely want to live in this country.

2 **Emma** ³Will / Willed Tom be at the restaurant later today?

   Hannah No, he ⁴will / won't. He's on holiday in Spain.

3 **Jamal** How do you think cities ⁵will / won't change over the next 100 years?

   Sam I think more and more of them ⁶will to / will become environmentally friendly.

4 **Kate** New houses are great, but where ⁷'ll / will people go for recreation?

   Lana They ⁸will to / 'll build new parks and green areas on the other side of town.

2 ⭐⭐ **Complete the sentences using will or won't and the information in brackets.**

1 Saad won't go to university.
   (not go to university)

2 Jenna _____ .
   (become an architect)

3 People _____ .
   (live in space by 2100)

4 Maya _____ .
   (not write a book)

5 Cities _____ .
   (be more environmentally friendly in the next century)

6 Khalid _____ .
   (not live abroad when he's older)

3 ⭐⭐ **Complete the sentences with will, 'll or won't.**

1 She can write music for the piano. I reckon she 'll be a famous composer one day.

2 My grandparents are on holiday in France. They _____ see me in the school concert.

3 Andy is very good with money. I think he _____ become a millionaire in the next decade.

4 Cathy _____ play football this afternoon. She has to study instead.

5 _____ you marry someone famous in the future?

6 My friend and I are good at French and German. I'm sure we _____ study languages at university.

7 _____ people live on other planets one day?

4 ⭐⭐ **Write questions using will. Then match the questions 1–5 with the answers a–e.**

1 the next American president be a woman?
   Will the next American president be a woman?

2 who be the best racing driver next season?
   _____

3 Brazil win the next football World Cup?
   _____

4 what children study in the future?
   _____

5 where people live in the next millennium?
   _____

____ **a** I imagine more of them will study computer programming and foreign languages.

__1__ **b** No, I reckon it'll be a man again.

____ **c** Lewis Hamilton, maybe. He's a great driver.

____ **d** I don't know, maybe in houses under the sea!

____ **e** Yes, I'm pretty sure they will. They've got a great team.

5 ⭐⭐⭐ **Write predictions about the things below. Use the phrases below and will or won't.**

I imagine (that) …	I'm pretty sure (that) …
I reckon (that) …	Maybe …

A famous person
I'm pretty sure that Brad Pitt won't be the next James Bond.

Computers

Cities

The world in 2500

Travel into space

The World Cup

Describing places

1 ⭐ **Match the words 1–10 with the pictures A–J.**

1	deserted	6	historic
2	flat	7	clean
3	modern	8	crowded
4	polluted	9	rural
5	urban	10	hilly

A |10

B |
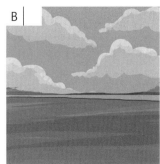

C |

D |

E |
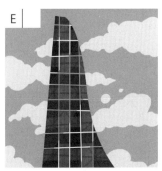

F |

G |

H |

I |

J |

2 ✪✪ **Complete the conversations with words from exercise 1.**

1 A What's Dubai like? Are there a lot of historic buildings?
  B There are a few, but not a lot. There are a lot of ¹ _modern_ buildings, though.

2 A Is Songdo polluted?
  B No, it isn't. It's very ² _____ .

3 A Was Oxford Street crowded today?
  B No, it wasn't. The shops were closed and the street was ³ _____ .

4 A Is Istanbul flat?
  B No, it isn't. It's ⁴ _____ .

5 A Is your home town rural?
  B No, it isn't. It's ⁵ _____ .

3 ✪✪✪ **Describe the place in the photo. Write three sentences.**

1 ....
2 ....
3 ....

4 ✪✪✪ **Answer the questions about the place where you live. Write complete sentences.**

1 Do you live in an urban area or a rural area?

....

2 Which areas are polluted?

....

3 Which areas are historic?

....

4 Which areas are modern?

....

5 Is it mostly flat or mostly hilly?

....

First conditional

1 ✪ **Match the sentence halves.**

1 If I see Emma,   f

2 I'll eat it   ....

3 If Bill is late, ...

4 Dad will drive you there   ....

5 If it rains, ...

6 Faisal will come to lunch   ....

a if you invite him.

b if you really want to go.

c we won't have a picnic.

d if you don't want it.

e he'll miss the bus.

f I'll give her the news.

2 ✪✪ **Rewrite these sentences so that they start with _If_.**

1 We'll stay at home if it rains tomorrow.
  If _it rains tomorrow, we'll stay at home._

2 They'll be hungry if they don't have breakfast.
  If ....
  ....

3 He'll catch the bus if he runs.
  If ....
  ....

4 Will you go to the cinema if it's sunny?
  If ....
  .... ?

5 She will help if you ask her.
  If ....
  ....

6 Will you say 'hello' if you see him?
  If ....
  .... ?

3 ✪✪ **Complete the sentences with the words below.**

| don't go don't pass see snows |
| will be will you say 'll win |

1 If you _don't go_ to bed, you'll be tired.

2 If Ed phones, what .... to him?

3 Marian .... angry if we're late.

4 What will you do if you .... your exams?

5 If I .... a book about Formula One in the shops, I'll buy it.

6 If they train every day, they .... the match.

7 If it .... today, we won't go for a walk.

4 ✪✪ **Complete the sentences using the correct form of the verbs in brackets.**

Smart city living

Overpopulation in cities causes a lot of problems, but if we [1] _make_ (make) our cities more environmentally friendly, we [2] .... (solve) some of those problems. Here are a few ideas:

- The roads [3] .... (not be) crowded with cars if we [4] .... (walk) and cycle.

- If we [5] .... (use) renewable energy, we [6] .... (make) less pollution.

- We [7] .... (not travel) long distances for shopping or work if we [8] .... (plan) buildings with shops, flats and offices.

What do you think? If we [9] .... (make) changes now, [10] .... (we / improve) our cities?

5 ✪✪✪ **Complete the sentences with your own ideas.**

1 If we all study very hard, ...
  ....

2 I'll phone my best friend today if ....
  ....

3 My dad won't give me any money if ....
  ....

4 If I don't tidy my room this evening, ...
  ....

5 If my favourite team win the match, ...
  ....

6 If the weather's good at the weekend, ...
  ....

7 If I have enough time, ...
  ....

Writing

A report on a survey

LANGUAGE FOCUS | *nobody* and *everybody*

1 ✪ **Choose the correct words.**

1 Everybody **understand** / ~~**understands**~~ the questions in the survey.
2 More than half of the people from the survey **believe** / **believes** that children will be taller in the next century.
3 Everybody **has got** / **have got** an opinion about the future.
4 One or two people **want** / **wants** to visit a different planet.
5 Some people **think** / **thinks** that there will be more deserts in the future.
6 Nobody **know** / **knows** the answer to the problem.
7 Most people **worry** / **worries** about the future.

2 ✪✪ **Complete the sentences with the words below.**

~~Everybody~~   Nobody   of   or   people   Some of

1 __Everybody__ believes there will be environmental problems in the future.
2 One _____ two students enjoy reading newspaper articles about the future.
3 _____ thinks the future will be exactly the same as the present.
4 Most _____ the students talk to their friends about the future of the planet.
5 Most _____ are worried about the future of tigers.
6 _____ us watch programmes about wild animals.

TASK | A report on a survey

3 ✪✪ **Complete the email. Use the information in the chart and *will*.**

	1	2	3	4	5	6	7	8
Will *The X Factor* become less popular?	✓	✓	✓	✓	✓	✓	✓	✓
Will there be more sport on TV?		✓		✓	✓		✓	
Will we get more TV channels?	✓	✓	✓		✓		✓	✓
Will there be more football on TV?	✓				✓			✓
Will we have better programmes for teenagers?		✓					✓	
Will there be lots more advertisements?	✓		✓	✓	✓	✓		✓
Will children definitely watch less TV in the future?	✓	✓	✓	✓	✓	✓	✓	✓

Hi, Cathy!

How's your new school? Do you like your teachers?

After class yesterday we went to the park with our friends – Sarah, Kate, Andy, Jack and all the others. There were eight of us. We started chatting about the future of TV programmes and we talked for more than an hour! Everybody thinks that *The X Factor* [1] __will become less popular__ in the future. Kate and I prefer *Britain's Got Talent*. It's much more interesting! Half of us reckon that [2] _____ . Most people say that [3] _____ . And some people think that [4] _____ .
Oh dear! I hate football! [5] _____ better programmes for teenagers, but I'm not sure about that. The rest of us say that [6] _____ – how boring!
Everybody says that [7] _____ more TV in the future. What do you think?

From,

Sue

4 ✪✪✪ **Write an email to a friend about the opinions of a group of people on the future of music, film or sports stars. Use the text in exercise 3 as a model. Write 100–150 words.**

READING Cities of the future

1 Read the text on page 73 of the Student's Book again. Answer the questions.

1 What do these numbers refer to?
- 3% ....
- 75% ....
- over 35 million ....

2 What problems are caused by overpopulation? Give two from the text.
- ....
- ....

3 According to the text, how can governments solve the problem of overpopulation?
....

I can understand an article about the growth of cities.

☹ 😐 🙂

VOCABULARY

2 Complete the names of places in towns and cities. Then answer the question.

| car park   crossing   high-rise   petrol   retail   space |

1 .... park
2 multi-storey ....
3 .... building
4 pedestrian ....
5 .... station
6 green ....

Describe one of these places from your home town or city.
....

I can describe a town or city I know.

☹ 😐 🙂

3 Choose one of the adjectives and write the name of a place you know next to it. The adjective should describe the place.

1 urban / rural ....
2 historic / modern ....
3 crowded / deserted ....
4 hilly / flat ....
5 polluted / clean ....

I can describe places.

☹ 😐 🙂

GRAMMAR

4 Complete the conversation with *will*, *'ll* or *won't* and the correct form of the verbs in brackets.

A What do you think [1] will happen (happen) to the city over the next 50 years?

B I think more people [2] .... (migrate) here.

A [3] .... that .... (cause) a lot of problems?

B It's possible, but we [4] .... (use) more renewable energy, so we [5] .... (not have) big problems with air pollution.

A Hmm, maybe you're right.

I can say what I think will happen in the future.

☹ 😐 🙂

5 Choose the correct words to complete the text.

If more people [1]**migrate / will migrate** to cities, there [2]**are / will be** more cars on the streets. If there [3]**are / will** be more cars on the streets, there [4]**is / will be** more pollution. Also, the roads [5]**are / will be** very crowded, but people [6]**will drive / drive less** and walk more if the roads [7]**become / will become** very crowded. If people [8]**will drive / drive less** and [9]**walk / will walk** more, there [10]**is / will be** less pollution.

I can talk about conditions and their results.

☹ 😐 🙂

SPEAKING

6 Number the conversation in the correct order 1–7.

A .... **Omar** Let me think ... Yes, I do.

B .... **Fahad** I disagree with you.

C .... **Fahad** I think it'll be a worse place because it will be more polluted.

D .... **Fahad** Do you think that our city will be a better place in the future?

E .... **Fahad** Why's that?

F .... **Omar** What do you think then?

G .... **Omar** Because I think we're improving the city a lot these days.

I can give my opinions about the future.

☹ 😐 🙂

Project

1 Match the headings 1–4 with the paragraphs A–D.

1 Transport   2 Energy   3 Food   4 Housing

FUTURE CITY

A | 4

The city will be crowded, so people will live in very tall skyscrapers, but the skyscrapers will have green spaces around them. The flats will be very modern.

B |

Offices and flats will be near to each other, so most people will walk or cycle from home to work. There won't be many cars on the roads, so the air will be clean.

C |

SUPER MARKET

Some food will come from far away and be sold in supermarkets, but some food will come from the city. The green spaces will be used to grow fruit and vegetables. These will be sold in local markets.

D |

The city will get its electricity from renewable energy. Every skyscraper will make solar and wind power. The river will make water power.

2 Make a poster about your ideas for a future city. Follow the steps in the project checklist.

- Write about transport, food, energy, housing, entertainment and recreation, and / or your own ideas.
- Find or draw pictures to illustrate your ideas.

TALK ABOUT IT

3 Exchange your posters with your classmates. How are the ideas similar? How are they different?

> Both our future cities will use renewable energy.

> In my future city, there will be cars on the roads, but in Nasir's city people will only use trains.

Sport for all

Can sport change your life?

A Darius Knight was born in 1990. He grew up in a poor part of south London where there was a lot of crime and other problems. His father was often in prison when he was young and his ¹ _situation_ was very difficult. But today Darius is a champion. He ² _____ in international tournaments all over the world and he wins a lot of trophies and medals. So what happened to change his life? Well, it has something to do with table tennis.

B Darius first tried table tennis at a local youth club. Gideon Ashison, the trainer, noticed he had a particular talent for the sport and wanted to ³ _____ him. He gave Darius and some other children extra lessons and they started training in a garden shed. Darius joined a table tennis club, started to enter local competitions and usually won.

C Before long the National Table Tennis Academy contacted him and invited him to practise there. The facilities and the coaches and instructors were excellent. Darius soon became a serious international ⁴ _____ . In 2005, when he was 15, he won a gold medal at the European Youth ⁵ _____ , and since then he has won several UK national titles.

D Darius is proud of his career and he and his coaching team are confident that he will win many more tournaments. He's going to keep on training hard and hopes that he'll be an Olympic champion. His story shows that sport really can change your life!

1 ✪ **Complete the article with five of the words below.**

| atmosphere | Championships | competes |
| competitor | fan | massive | ~~situation~~ | support |

2 ✪ **Read the article again. Match the headings 1–4 with the paragraphs A–D.**

1 _D_ Hopes for the future
2 ____ Darius – past and present
3 ____ The journey to success
4 ____ How it began

3 ✪✪ **Correct the sentences.**

1 Darius lived in a ~~rich~~ part of south London.
   Darius lived in a poor part of south London.

2 Darius had a good childhood.
   ....
   ....

3 Darius competes in tournaments only in the UK.
   ....
   ....

4 Darius had extra table tennis lessons at school.
   ....
   ....

5 He finished second at the 2005 European Youth Championships.
   ....
   ....

4 ✪✪ **Complete the sentences with words from the article.**

1 Darius was born in _1990_ .
2 _____ first noticed Darius's talent.
3 _____ invited Darius to practise there.
4 The facilities at the academy were _____ .
5 Darius was _____ when he won the European Youth Championships.
6 Darius' goal for the future is to become _____ .

5 ✪✪✪ **Answer the questions.**

1 How was life difficult for Darius when he was young?
   ....

2 Why did Gideon Ashison start giving Darius extra lessons?
   ....

3 What did the National Table Tennis Academy invite Darius to do?
   ....

4 How does Darius feel about his career in table tennis?
   ....

5 Do you admire Darius? Why / Why not?
   ....

6 Would you like a career in sport? Why / Why not?
   ....

Vocabulary

People in sport

1 ⭐ **Match a word with a picture.**

> loser ~~champion~~ referee
> reporter supporter manager

1 _champion_

2 _____

3 _____

4 _____

5 _____

6 _____

2 ⭐⭐ **Complete the sentences with the words from exercise 1.**

1 The winner of a sports competition is the _champion_ .

2 A _____ is a company which gives money to a sports team.

3 A _____ works for a newspaper, magazine or TV company.

4 When you want a team or sportsperson to win, you're a _____ .

5 When you don't win a game, you're the _____ .

6 A _____ controls the game and makes sure all the players follow the rules.

3 ⭐⭐ **Do the *Famous people in sport* quiz. Choose the best word to complete each sentence.**

Famous people in sport

1 David Beckham was ... of the English football team from 2000 to 2006.

  a sponsor **b** captain **c** supporter

2 Roger Federer was a ... at the 2008 Wimbledon Tennis Championship.

  a finalist **b** supporter **c** referee

3 Runner Usain Bolt has a ... who organises his training and competitions.

  a journalist **b** manager **c** champion

4 According to a survey from 2012, Manchester United Football Club has 659,000,000 ... around the world!

  a reporters **b** losers **c** supporters

5 For many years, the Williams sisters' father was their tennis ... .

  a finalist **b** coach **c** champion

6 The sports clothes company Reebok is a big ... of many sports.

  a reporter **b** manager **c** sponsor

VOCABULARY BUILDER | **Expressions with *have***

4 ⭐⭐ **Choose the correct words.**

1 I had **fun** / **a rest** / **a chat** playing tennis.

2 Emir and Fahad had **an argument** / **a go** / **fun** about which football team is the best.

3 Would you like to have **a rest** / **an argument** / **a go** at driving a Formula 1 car?

4 Aleena and Tina had **a go** / **a chat** / **a rest** about their plans for the week.

5 I was tired, so I had **an argument** / **a chat** / **a rest** after school yesterday.

5 ⭐⭐⭐ **Answer the questions.**

1 What famous sportsperson would you most like to have a chat with? Why?

_____

_____

2 Would you like to have a go at being a sports reporter? Which sports would you report on?

_____

_____

be going to

1 ✪ **Choose the correct words.**

1 The owner (is going) / are going to look for a new manager.
2 I'm **not / don't** going to play football tomorrow.
3 We **going not / aren't going** to watch the tennis match.
4 Mohammed **going / is going** to be captain next year.
5 Cathy and Emma **is going / are going** to choose a new sponsor.
6 **We / We're** going to play table tennis tomorrow morning.

2 ✪✪ **Complete the sentences. Use the information in the chart and the words in brackets.**

	after school	at the weekend	next week
Dan	go shopping (with Ed)	play football	play tennis (with Tom)
Tom	send emails	go swimming	play tennis (with Dan)
Ed	go shopping (with Dan)	watch motor racing on TV	have a go at table tennis

1 Dan 's going to go shopping after school. (after school)
2 Dan isn't going to go swimming at the weekend. He's going to play football. (go swimming / at the weekend)
3 Tom .... (at the weekend)
4 Tom .... (go shopping / after school)
5 Ed .... (next week)
6 Ed .... (play football / at the weekend)
7 Dan and Ed .... (after school)
8 Dan and Tom .... (go shopping / next week)

3 ✪✪✪ **Write two positive and two negative sentences about your plans. Use *be going to* and some of the words below.**

after school   at the weekend   in two weeks
later   next week   on Saturday   tonight

Positive
1 ....
2 ....

Negative
3 ....
4 ....

will and be going to

4 ✪✪ **Complete the conversations with the correct form of *will* or *be going to* and the verbs below.**

be   buy   ~~have~~   make   pass   win

1 A Do you have plans for the weekend?
   B Yes, we [1] 're going to have a picnic.
2 A Your mobile phone looks quite old!
   B Yes, I know. I [2] .... a new one when I have enough money.
3 A I'm nervous about my exam next week.
   B Oh, you [3] .... OK. I'm sure you [4] .... easily.
4 A I [5] .... a coffee. Would you like one?
   B Yes, thanks – black with one sugar, please.
5 A Who do you think [6] .... the next World Cup?
   B Brazil, of course!

5 ✪✪✪ **Write about your plans and predictions for the future. Use *will* and *be going to* and some of the expressions in the box.**

after (university)   at (half past eight)   in (2050)
in (May)   in the future   next (Tuesday)
on (Wednesday)   one day   tonight

Plans
1 ....
2 ....

Predictions
3 ....
4 ....

Vocabulary

Sports: collocations

1 ⭐ **Complete the collocations with the words below.**

> court match race season
> ~~stadium~~ star team trophy

1 football
   stadium

2 motor racing
   ....

3 rugby
   ....

4 tennis
   ....

5 skiing
   ....

6 cycling
   ....

7 basketball
   ....

8 running
   ....

2 ⭐⭐ **Choose the correct words.**

My family love sport and we do it all the time. Next weekend, my brother is in a ten-kilometre **¹race**/ **running** / **tournament**. On the same day, my sister is playing in a **²tennis** / **skiing** / **golf** match. She's a finalist in our town's tennis **³race** / **court** / **tournament**! In the winter, during the **⁴athletics** / **skiing** / **trophy** season, we always go to France for a week. That's the one sport that we do together, as a family. My brother loves team sports. He's playing in a **⁵rugby** / **golf** / **cycling** match next weekend. He also likes football. Last weekend, his football team won a match at the big football **⁶race** / **course** / **stadium** in our town. About 5000 people were watching! And me? I'm in a cycling **⁷match** / **race** / **course** this afternoon!

3 ⭐⭐ **Correct the sport in each sentence.**

1 Kobe Bryant is a ~~cycling~~ star for the Los Angeles Lakers.
   basketball

2 The Formula 1 Grand Prix is a golf tournament.
   ....

3 The World Cup is a famous athletics trophy.
   ....

4 Tiger Woods is a tennis champion.
   ....

5 The London Marathon is a 42-km cycling race through London.
   ....

6 Serena Williams is a basketball player.
   ....

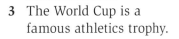

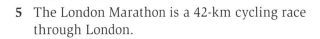

4 ⭐⭐⭐ **Write four sentences about famous sports people, places or events. Use collocations from exercises 1 to 3.**

Wembley is a football stadium.

1 ....

2 ....

3 ....

4 ....

be going to: questions

1 ✪ **Choose the correct words.**

1 Where **is** / **are** you going to play?
2 **Is** / **Are** you going to have a go at golf?
3 Who are you **to going** / **going to** meet at the stadium?
4 What are you going to **wearing** / **wear** on Saturday?
5 Which team are you **go** / **going** to support?
6 Are you going to travel by train? Yes, I **is** / **am**.

2 ✪✪ **Complete the questions with** *be going to*. **Then write answers using the information in brackets.**

1 A _Are_ they _going to_ lose?
  B _No, they aren't._ (no)

2 A Where .... you .... practise?
  B ....
  .... (at the athletics stadium)

3 A .... we .... watch the match?
  B ....
  .... (yes)

4 A What time .... it .... start?
  B ....
  .... (5 o'clock)

5 A Who .... she .... support?
  B ....
  .... (Bayern Munich)

6 A .... they .... sponsor the team?
  B ....
  .... (no)

7 A .... you .... buy a ticket?
  B ....
  .... (yes)

8 A When .... he .... play?
  B ....
  .... (on Tuesday)

9 A Where .... they .... have the 2020 Olympics?
  B ....
  .... (Tokyo)

3 ✪✪✪ **Rafael Nadal is going to play in a tennis match tomorrow. Write questions for him using** *be going to*.

1 Who _are you going to play_
   against in the match tomorrow?
2 When .... ?
3 Where .... ?
4 What .... ?
5 Are .... ?

Present continuous for future arrangements

4 ✪✪ **Complete the conversation using the present continuous.**

Jenna What [1] _are you doing_ (you do) this summer?

Tom [2] .... (I not do) anything special. Are you?

Jenna Yes. [3] .... (we fly) to London to watch a tennis tournament with our English cousins.

Tom [4] .... (you meet) them there?

Jenna Yes, [5] .... (we spend) a week with them. Then, [6] .... (we go) to the seaside.

Tom That sounds great. [7] .... (I not go) away at all. I haven't got any money, so [8] .... (I work) in my dad's shop for the summer.

5 ✪✪✪ **Write five sentences about your future arrangements. Use the present continuous.**

I'm playing football with my friends tomorrow.

1 ....
2 ....
3 ....
4 ....
5 ....

A formal letter

LANGUAGE FOCUS | Layout and language in a formal letter

1 ✪ Complete the gaps A–E in the letter with the words below.

| ~~12 Scope Road~~   14th November 2015   James Goodwin   Manager   Sir or Madam |

2 ✪✪ Correct the mistakes 1–9 in the letter.

A 12 Scope Road

Bristol, England

B ....

¹Dears **C** .... ,

I am the manager of an athletics club in Bristol, England. The name of the club is Star Athletes. I am ²write to you because we are planning a tournament and we are looking for sponsors.

The tournament will take place ³on April. Teams and fans from four countries ⁴going to be in Bristol for this event, and I think that it ⁵will to be good publicity for your company.

Please ⁶contacting me if you are interested in sponsoring us, or if you ⁷needs any more information.

I look forward to ⁸hear from you.

⁹Your faithfully,

D ....

E ....

---

1 Dear	4	7 ....
2	5	8 ....
3	6	9 ....

TASK | A formal letter

3 ✪✪ You are going to write a formal letter to a photographer. Your letter should have a paragraph for each of the notes below. Number the notes 1–3 in the order you should include them in your letter.

.... Please contact me.

.... Captain / Club name. Looking for a photographer to take pictures of cycling team for new club brochure.

.... Club will send brochure to a lot of schools – good publicity for you.

4 ✪✪✪ Write the letter to the photographer. Use the writing guide below and the information in exercise 3.

Greenbank Road

Exeter, England

[Date]

Dear Sir or Madam,

[Paragraph 1]

[Paragraph 2]

[Paragraph 3]

Yours faithfully,

[Name]

Captain, Hotwheels Cycling Team

9 Self-evaluation

Review Unit 9 in the Student's Book and complete the exercises below. Think about your progress and choose one of the faces.

READING Driving ambition

1 Read the text on page 83 of the Student's Book again. Answer the questions.

1 Find similar words in the text for the following words:
- raced against ....
- very popular ....
- help ....

2 What does Karen say about female racing drivers in the past, present and future?
Past: ....
Present: ....
Future: ....

3 What does Karen say about motor racing in the UK?
....
....

> I can understand an interview with a sportsperson.

VOCABULARY

2 Circle the odd one out. Then use the circled word in a sentence.

1 champion   finalist   loser
....

2 football   player   referee
....

3 match   fan   supporter
....

4 sponsor   match   tournament
....

> I can talk about people in sport.

3 Choose the correct words to complete the sport collocations.

1 running (race)/ football
2 skiing **rugby** / **season**
3 golf **course** / **stadium**
4 motor **racing** / **court**
5 basketball **course** / **star**

Use one of the collocations in a sentence.
....
....

> I can talk about sport.

GRAMMAR

4 Look at the photos. Write one more prediction and two plans. Use *will* or *be going to*.

Predictions		Plans	
1 Friday	**2** Brazil!	**3** Fahad	**4** Lisa

1 ....
2 ....
3 ....
4 ....

> I can talk about plans and predictions.

5 Make questions with *be going to*. Then answer the questions.

1 What / you / do tomorrow?
....
....

2 When / you / eat dinner?
....
....

3 you / watch TV next week?
....
....

> I can talk about future arrangements.

SPEAKING

6 Write answers for the questions.

1 A Are you doing anything this evening?
  B ....

2 A I'm going to a football match next week. Do you fancy going?
  B ....

3 A Tonight is the basketball game. Shall I meet you at 6 o'clock?
  B ....

4 A Where's the football match on?
  B ....

> I can invite a friend and make arrangements.

1 The main character in *The Thirty-Nine Steps* is called Hannay. Read the first paragraph of the story. What do you think happened next?

1 Hannay stopped the car and spoke to the policeman.

2 Hannay drove faster and got out of the village quickly.

3 Suddenly, a car appeared in front of him.

2 Read the extract and answer the questions.

1 What was the policeman doing when Hannay came into the village?

2 Why didn't Hannay stop for the policeman?

3 Why did he think it was stupid to steal the car?

4 Why did he drive off the road into a hedge?

5 Why didn't he fall into the river with the car?

3 Answer the questions. Look at the extract, and use your own words and ideas.

1 Why do you think the police were chasing Hannay?

2 Who or what do you think the Black Stone was?

3 How do you think Hannay felt when he heard the plane?

4 Why was Hannay pleased about losing the car?

4 Buchan uses the simile *like a knife through butter* to mean 'very easily'. We use similes to compare things, using the words *like* or *as*. Match 1–5 with a–e to make similes.

1 as white   a the wind
2 eat like   b as snow
3 as big   c as fire
4 run like   d a horse
5 as hot   e as a bus

I came into a village and I saw a policeman standing outside the Post Office and reading something carefully. He looked up at the car, and stepped into the road, and held up a hand to stop me.

I almost did stop. But then I realized that the policeman had been reading about me. I supposed the police at the hotel had worked quickly and contacted all the local villages. I drove faster, the policeman jumped out of my way, and I was soon out of the village.

I left the main road as soon as possible and tried a smaller one. It was not easy without a map, and I realized that I had been stupid to steal the car. It would help the police and the Black Stone to find me in any corner of Scotland. If I left it, and went off on foot, they would find me in an hour or two.

I took a road that went along a narrow valley, and then up into the moor again. I was very hungry; I had eaten nothing since morning. And now, as I drove, I heard a noise in the sky, and there was the plane.

On the moor it would see me in a minute. I drove as fast as I could down into another valley and towards a wood. Suddenly, a car appeared in front of me from a side road. There was no time to stop. I did the only thing possible and drove off the road into a hedge, hoping to hit something soft beyond. But I was out of luck. The car went through the hedge like a knife through butter, and immediately began to fall. I jumped out and was caught by the branch of a tree, while the car disappeared into a river fifteen metres below.

A hand helped me out of the tree, and a frightened voice asked me if I was badly hurt. The speaker was a young man who was very alarmed and very sorry. I was more pleased than angry; it was a good way for the car to disappear.

From *The Thirty-Nine Steps*, Oxford Bookworms. Retold by Nick Bullard.

The Best Roller Coasters by Ann Brookes

I've been on 25 roller coasters in eight different countries. Why do I love them? That's easy – they're fast and exciting! I've never found a ride which I'm frightened to try.

I think the scariest roller coaster that I've tried is 'Oblivion' at Alton Towers in the UK. You get into a special car and it climbs up to the top of the roller coaster. You stop for three seconds, and then you go down nearly 60 metres! You get a real feeling that you're falling and going to die. I've taken about 50 photos of 'Oblivion'.

My sister's been on it once, but she refused to go again – she almost ¹ fainted . My mum won't try the rides at all. She says they make her ² .... I think she's got a ³ .... and really can't ⁴ .... with them. She says it's worse than getting a ⁵ .... at the dentist! So I normally go on the roller coasters with my friends.

The roller coaster that I've visited the most is 'Furius Baco' in PortAventura, Spain. I've had three family holidays near PortAventura, and we've been there five times now. You travel from 0 to 135 kilometres an hour in 3.5 seconds, and your body feels really weird. You go upside down and look up at the sky – you can lose your money if you aren't careful!

The biggest and fastest roller coasters in the world are in the US and Japan. I've asked my mum and dad about going on holiday there, but they think my love of roller coasters is ridiculous!

1 ✪ **Complete the text with five of the words below.**

> cancel   check-up   cope   dizzy   ~~fainted~~
> filling   patient   phobia   specialist

2 ✪ **Read the text again. Tick (✓) the correct box.**

Ann describes her experiences on roller coasters in … .

a ☐ Japan and Spain

b ☐ Spain and the UK

c ☐ the UK and Japan

3 ✪✪ **Read the text again. Choose the correct answers.**

1 Ann has been on roller coasters in … countries.
  a five   (b eight)   c 25

2 The 'Oblivion' ride is at Alton Towers in … .
  a Spain   b the UK   c PortAventura

3 Ann's sister thought 'Oblivion' was very … .
  a fast   b exciting   c scary

4 Ann has stayed near PortAventura … times.
  a five   b 50   c three

5 On 'Furius Baco' your … feels very strange.
  a hair   b neck   c body

6 Your speed on 'Furius Baco' … .
  a changes very fast
  b is always 135 kms an hour
  c goes to 5 kms an hour in 3.5 seconds

4 ✪✪✪ **Answer the questions.**

1 Why does Ann like roller coasters?

2 Why is 'Oblivion' so scary?

3 Why doesn't Ann's mum like roller coasters?

4 Why does Ann normally go on the roller coasters with her friends and not her family?

5 Why does Ann want to go on holiday to the US and Japan?

6 What do Ann's parents think about her love of roller coasters?

7 Do you like roller coasters? Why / Why not?

8 Would you like to go on 'Oblivion' or 'Furius Baco'? Why / Why not?

Vocabulary

Feelings

1 ⭐ **Match the words 1–8 with the pictures A–H.**

1 enthusiastic   A
2 embarrassed   ....
3 fond   ....
4 interested   ....
5 keen   ....
6 stressed   ....
7 terrified   ....
8 worried   ....

A

B

C

D

E

F

Bungee jumping

G

Exam starts: 2.00
Revision

H

2 ✪✪ **Complete the text with the words from exercise 1.**

Penfriend page

My name's Emir and I'm ¹ interested in finding a penfriend. I'm 15 and I live in England. My family are very ² .... of travelling. We've been to Spain, Russia and France. Next year, we're going to Italy.

I'm really ³ .... about studying languages. I speak Spanish, French and German. I'm not very good at German, so I'm ⁴ .... on practising it with my new German penfriend. I don't really get ⁵ .... out about making mistakes. My parents and sister are ⁶ .... of speaking foreign languages, so they let me do all the talking when we travel!

Everybody in my family loves football and our favourite team is Sheffield United. We're a little ⁷ .... about supporting them right now because they've had a terrible season. We're a bit ⁸ .... about the club's future.

What about you? What do you like doing?

Write soon!

Emir

VOCABULARY BUILDER | Modifiers

3 ✪✪ **Put the modifiers in the correct place in each sentence.**

1 I'm not ⋀ fond of swimming. (very)
         very
2 Max is worried about his driving test. (really)
3 Tom is interested in science. (not very)
4 My mother is fond of spiders. (not at all)
5 Liz is stressed out about her exams. (quite)
6 He's enthusiastic about languages. (very)

4 ✪✪✪ **Answer the questions about yourself. Use modifiers.**

1 How keen are you on watching football on TV?

....

2 How stressed out do you feel about your school work?

....

3 What school subjects are you interested in?

....

4 How fond are you of sweet foods?

....

Present perfect: positive and negative

1 ✪ **Choose the correct words.**

1   I haven't **try** / **tried** skiing.
2   She's **helped** / **helping** Aleena with her homework a few times.
3   I've **flew** / **flown** in a plane.
4   They **haven't** / **don't** spoken with Tom.
5   We've **been** / **were** in the garden all day.
6   The weather **is** / **has** been sunny recently.

2 ✪✪ **Complete the chart.**

base form	past participle
become	¹ become
²	chatted
do	³
⁴	found
⁵	fainted
fly	⁶
⁷	heard
leave	⁸
sleep	⁹
speak	¹⁰

3 ✪✪ **Rewrite the sentences in the negative form.**

1   She's been on a roller coaster before.
    She hasn't been on a roller coaster before.
2   He's seen a specialist about his phobia.

3   Fahad's spoken to a doctor.

4   I've visited the dentist this month.

5   They've gone to Paris by plane.

6   Khalid's had exams this week.

4 ✪✪ **Complete the sentences with the present perfect form of the verbs below.**

| find   improve   not eat   not fly   not speak   ~~write~~ |

1   Lana has written several emails to her grandmother.
2   Saad .... with his teacher about his exam results.
3   Maya and Tina .... some money in the park.
4   We .... in a hot-air balloon.
5   Your English .... a lot this year!
6   You .... Mexican food.

5 ✪✪ **Complete the news article with the present perfect form of the verbs in brackets.**

Frog salad

A housewife from Sheffield ¹ has won (win) a court case against her local supermarket after she bought a bag of salad which contained a frog. Mary Lewis opened the bag and started to empty the salad onto plates when a live frog fell out. 'I ² .... (not be) so shocked in all my life,' she told reporters. Since then, Mrs Lewis ³ .... (develop) a serious phobia about frogs, and she ⁴ .... (stop) eating salads as well. 'I ⁵ .... (try) to eat salad two or three times recently, but it's impossible. It just reminds me of that horrible frog,' she said. 'I ⁶ .... (shop) at that supermarket for 20 years, but never again.'

6 ✪✪✪ **Write sentences about things you have and haven't done. Use the present perfect.**

Things you have done:
    I've written a letter to a famous person.
1   ....
2   ....
3   ....

Things you haven't done:
    I haven't visited France.
4   ....
5   ....
6   ....

Injuries

1 ⭐ **Match the words 1–6 with the photos A–F.**

1 a scratch   _F_
2 a bruise   ....
3 a sprain   ....
4 a cut   ....
5 a burn   ....
6 a break   ....

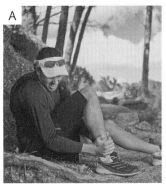
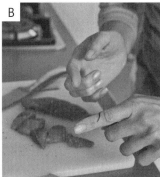
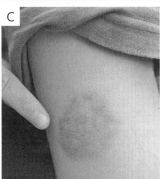
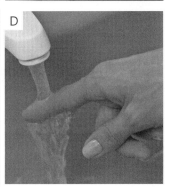
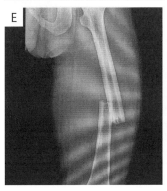
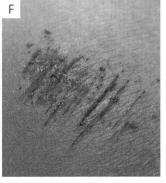

2 ⭐⭐ **Correct the mistakes.**

1 My little brother found a knife and ~~cutted~~ his finger.   _cut_ ....
2 Be careful with that hot food from the microwave. Don't burnt your hand.
   ....
3 Ivana has break her big toe again. That's the second time this year!   ....
4 I fell off a rock in the mountains and now I've got this bruised on my leg.   ....
5 He can't play rugby this weekend because he's got a really bad knee injured.   ....
6 Oh, no! I think I've sprain my ankle.
   ....

3 ⭐⭐ **Choose the correct words.**

1 She walked into a chair and now she's got a big, blue **burn** / (**bruise**) / **cut** on her leg.
2 Oh, no! I've **cut** / **sprained** / **burnt** my finger with the knife.
3 He's been on the beach for hours and he's **bruised** / **burnt** / **injured** his face.
4 The best player in their team can't play because he's **broken** / **cut** / **injured**.
5 She's been in hospital for five days because she's **broken** / **bruised** / **scratched** her leg.
6 Faisal has got a nasty ankle **bruised** / **injury** / **sprained**.

4 ⭐⭐ **Complete the sentences with the words below.**

> broken bruised burn ~~cut~~ injured sprained

1 The window was broken, so Joe was careful. He didn't want to _cut_ his hand.
2 He's .... his arm on a skiing holiday. He needs to go to hospital.
3 A lot of people were .... in the train crash. They had terrible cuts and bruises.
4 She's fallen off her bike and she's .... her arm. It's black and blue.
5 Wait! Don't eat the soup. It's very hot. You don't want to .... your mouth.
6 I fell and I .... my ankle while I was playing rugby.

5 ⭐⭐⭐ **Complete the email with the correct words.**

Dear Suzy,

I'm in Thailand on an adventure holiday. It's beautiful here, but I'm having a terrible time!

The weather is very hot and I've [1] _burnt_ my nose in the sun.

Yesterday, I walked into a tree! I've [2] .... my face under my eye – it's all black and blue! And this morning I broke a glass bottle and I've got a big, red [3] .... on my hand!

Last week, one of the girls in our group fell while we were climbing a mountain. The doctor looked at her arm and said it was [4] .... because she couldn't move it. She needed to go to hospital and now she's gone back to the UK. I feel very sorry for her. I think I'm going to stay in my tent for the last week of the trip! I don't want another [5] .... !

See you,

Hannah

10 Grammar

Present perfect: questions

1 ✪ **Choose the correct words.**

1 (Have)/ **Has** you seen that new film? It's scary!
2 **Have** / **Has** Jamal been to Alton Towers?
3 Has Samir ever **be** / **been** bungee jumping?
4 **A** Has Sue been to a specialist?
  B No, she **hasn't** / **haven't**.
5 Has Talib ever **broken** / **break** a bone?
6 **A** Have you had a phobia of spiders for long?
  B Yes, I **have** / **has**.

2 ✪✪ **Complete the conversations with the words below.**

ever been   ever   ~~has~~   have gone
haven't   they have

1 **A** ¹ _Has_ anyone swum across the Atlantic Ocean?
  B No, they ² _____ . It's impossible.
2 **A** Has a woman ³ _____ to the moon?
  B No, only men. But women ⁴ _____ into space.
3 **A** Have the Olympic Games ⁵ _____ been held in Australia?
  B Yes, ⁶ _____ . They were held in Sydney in 2000.

3 ✪✪ **Complete the questions with *have* or *has* and the correct from of the verbs in brackets. Then match the questions 1–6 with answers a–f.**

1 _Have_ you _heard_ Basma's news? (hear)
2 _____ you _____ your finger? (bruise)
3 _____ your brother _____ anything dangerous? (do)
4 _____ we _____ the lesson? (finish)
5 _____ your dad _____ his ankle? (sprain)
6 _____ Marian ever _____ anything really frightening? (do)

a Yes, I have. My friend closed the door on it!
b Yes, I have. She's moving to a new house!   1
c No, she hasn't. She prefers relaxing things.
d No, he hasn't. He's broken it.
e Yes, he has. He's climbed an active volcano!
f No, we haven't. There are five more minutes.

4 ✪✪ **Write questions using *have / has* and *ever* and the words in brackets.**

1 _Have you ever seen a shark?_
  (you / see a shark)
2 _____
  (you / break your arm)
3 _____
  (your parents / go to the UK)
4 _____
  (the US / have a queen)
5 _____
  (your friend / ride a horse)
6 _____
  (you / meet a famous person)
7 _____
  (your teacher / go to Scotland)
8 _____
  (your friend / see an elephant)

5 ✪✪✪ **Write questions using *have / has* and *ever* using the words in the boxes. Then write short answers.**

best friend   brother   dad   parents
sister   teacher   your mum

appear   be   break   climb   meet   play   see   visit

Has your mum ever appeared on TV?
Yes, she has.

1 _____
  _____
2 _____
  _____
3 _____
  _____
4 _____
  _____
5 _____
  _____
6 _____
  _____

An informal email

1 ✪✪ **Put the sentences A–H in order 1–8 to make a short email.**

A .... Have you heard from Dave?

B _1_ Hi Kevin, how's it going?

C .... He couldn't remember anything, so they're doing some tests.

D .... Guess what! He's in hospital because he had an accident!

E .... I'll write soon with more news.

F .... He fell off his bike and hit his head.

G .... Tom

H .... See you,

2 ✪✪ **Complete the email with the words below.**

| back | because | been | ~~going~~ | guess | heard | interviewed | see | so | so |

Hi Phil,

How's it ¹ _going_ ? I'm fine, but I've got some news. Have you
² .... from Peter this week? ³ ....
what! He's ⁴ .... on TV! It rained a lot here last week,
and ⁵ .... the river got very high yesterday. Some
people were in their cars in the water. They were very scared
⁶ .... they couldn't get out. Peter rescued a woman
and her baby. ⁷ .... now he's a hero! Lots of journalists
have ⁸ .... him and he's been on the TV news. Wow!

Write ⁹ .... soon, Phil, and tell me your news.

¹⁰ .... you!

From,

Fahad

3 ✪✪✪ **Write an informal email. Use the text in exercise 2 as a model.**

- Use the information in these notes:
- Write 100–150 words.

  - People: Rob writing to Anna about Lisa
  - Situation: Lisa / climb up a tree / fall off
  - Problems: break leg / cut head
  - Help: phone the police
  - Now: in hospital until Sunday

Review Unit 10 in the Student's Book and complete the exercises below. Think about your progress and choose one of the faces.

READING Feel the fear!

1 **Read the text on page 91 of the Student's Book again. Answer the questions.**

1 What phobias does Yasmin mention? Write three.
- ....
- ....
- ....

2 How did the specialist help Yasmin with her phobia? Write three things.
- ....
- ....
- ....

I can understand a webpost about phobias.

VOCABULARY

2 **Correct the sentences. Then answer the question.**

1 I'm not keen of speaking in public.

....

2 I'm stressed out in my homework.

....

3 I'm not very fond by sweet foods.

....

4 I'm worried on the future. ....

Write a sentence about yourself, using one of the adjectives and prepositions.

....

I can describe my feelings.

3 **Choose the correct answers. Then answer the question.**

1 I broke my ... .
a arm b scratch c burn
2 Amber had a ... .
a burnt b sprained c bruise
3 Is your hand ... ?
a burnt b break c an injury
4 He's sprained his ... .
a ankle b face c hair

What injuries have you had? Describe one.

....

I can talk about injuries I've had.

GRAMMAR

4 **Look at the chart and write sentences. Use the present perfect.**

	✓	✗
Fatima and I	try sushi	write a book
Emma	faint	fly in a helicopter
Tom and Kevin	chat with a famous person	win a lot of money

1 Fatima and I have ....
We haven't ....
2 Emma ....
She ....
3 Tom and Kevin ....
They ....

I can talk about experiences.

5 **Write questions with the present perfect and *ever*.**

1 you / break a bone?

....

2 you / appear / on TV?

....

3 you / try / a strange foreign food?

....

4 you / write / a letter to a famous person?

....

I can ask about people's experiences.

SPEAKING

6 **Complete the conversation.**

happen   maybe   ~~OK~~   playing   sprained   wrong

A   Are you ¹ OK ?
B   Not really.
A   What's ² .... ?
B   I think I've ³ .... my ankle.
A   How did that ⁴ .... ?
B   I was ⁵ .... football in the gym.
A   ⁶ .... you need to phone your dad.

I can help someone with an injury.

1 Look at the information in the chart.
Then complete the text below.

What's your greatest fear?	
fears	**number of people**
spiders and insects	10
loud noises	8
heights	6
public speaking	4
storms	3

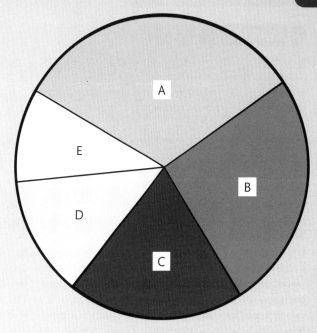

We wanted to find out what people are terrified
of, so we asked 31 people in our class to choose
their greatest fear from a list of five choices. The
most popular answer was ¹ spiders and insects ,
which ten people named as their greatest fear.
Next came ² .... , which is the
greatest fear of eight of our classmates. The third
greatest fear is ³ .... – for example,
tall buildings or high mountains. We were
interested to learn that most of us do not fear
public speaking. Only ⁴ .... people
named this as their greatest fear. Finally, in last
place, three people said that their greatest fear is
⁵ ....

A   spiders and insects ☐

B   loud noises ☐

C   heights ☐

D   public speaking ☐

E   storms ☐

2 Work in groups. Make a pie chart. Follow the steps
in the project checklist.

- Think of five fears. Make a list.
- Ask your classmates to choose their greatest fear from
  the list.
- Write down the number of choices for each fear.
- List the fears in the chart below.
- Write the number of people who chose each fear.
- Make a pie chart from the results.

What's your greatest fear?	
fears	**number of people**

TALK ABOUT IT ▮▮▮▮▷

3 Write and present your results to another group.
Use the text in exercise 1 as a model.

> The most popular answer was spiders and insects.

Words to learn

Words to learn is a list of all the target vocabulary from this level. Use this list to revise the vocabulary after you have finished each unit. ○━ a word from the Oxford 3000™ list

STARTER ■ ■ ■

above (prep) ○━ /ə'bʌv/ in a higher place: *The people in the flat above make a lot of noise.*

armchair (n) /'ɑːmtʃeə(r)/ a soft comfortable chair with arms which support your arms: *My dad's favourite armchair is next to the window.*

average (adj) /'ævərɪdʒ/ normal or typical: *He's average height for his age.*

bald (adj) /bɔːld/ having little or no hair on the head: *He went bald when he was only 30.*

beard (n) ○━ /bɪəd/ hair which grows on a man's cheeks and chin: *My uncle is going to grow a beard.*

bed (n) ○━ /bed/ a piece of furniture that you lie on when you sleep: *There are two beds in my bedroom.*

behind (prep) ○━ /bɪ'haɪnd/ in, at or to the back of something: *There's a small garden behind the house.*

between (prep) ○━ /bɪ'twiːn/ in the space in the middle of two things: *I was sitting between Amy and Tina.*

biology (n) ○━ /baɪ'ɒlədʒi/ the scientific study of living things: *We learnt about the life cycle of a frog in biology today.*

blond (adj) ○━ /blɒnd/ (a person) with fair or yellow hair: *Most of our family have blond hair.*

blue (adj) ○━ /bluː/ the colour of a clear sky on a sunny day: *Many Scandinavian people have blue eyes.*

bookcase (n) /'bʊkkeɪs/ a piece of furniture with shelves to keep books on: *I have a lot of books so I need a big bookcase.*

brown (adj) ○━ /braʊn/ having the colour of soil or wood: *They've both got brown eyes.*

chair (n) ○━ /tʃeə(r)/ a piece of furniture for one person to sit on: *There are eight chairs around the dining table.*

chemistry (n) ○━ /'kemɪstri/ the scientific study of the structure of substances: *We did an experiment in our chemistry lesson today.*

chest of drawers (n) ○━ /ˌtʃest əv 'drɔːz/ a piece of furniture with drawers to keep clothes in: *I keep most of my clothes in a chest of drawers.*

coffee table (n) ○━ /'kɒfi ˌteɪbl/ a small, low table: *There are some magazines on the coffee table in the living room.*

computer (n) ○━ /kəm'pjuːtə(r)/ an electronic machine that can store, find and arrange information: *I use a computer to go on the internet.*

cooker (n) ○━ /'kʊkə(r)/ a large piece of kitchen equipment for cooking using gas or electricity: *There's a pot of curry on the cooker.*

cupboard (n) ○━ /'kʌbəd/ a piece of furniture, usually with shelves inside and a door or doors at the front, used for storing food, clothes, etc.: *We keep our plates and glasses in the cupboard next to the sink.*

curly (adj) ○━ /'kɜːli/ (of hair) that is full of curls: *The actor is tall with blond, curly hair.*

dark (adj) ○━ /dɑːk/ having brown or black hair or skin: *She was small and dark with brown eyes.*

desk (n) ○━ /desk/ a type of table, often with drawers, that you sit at to write or work: *Have you got a desk in your room for doing your homework?*

English (n) ○━ /'ɪŋglɪʃ/ the study of the language spoken in the UK, the US and some other countries: *I'm learning English because I'd like to live in Australia one day.*

fair (adj) ○━ /feə(r)/ (used about the skin or hair) light in colour: *People with fair hair and skin need to be careful in the sun.*

French (n) ○━ /frentʃ/ the study of the language spoken in France and some other countries: *French and English are the official languages of Canada.*

fridge (n) ○━ /frɪdʒ/ a metal container with a door in which food, etc. is kept cold (but not frozen) so that it stays fresh: *Put the milk in the fridge, please.*

geography (n) ○━ /dʒi'ɒgrəfi/ the study of the countries of the world, and of their natural and physical features: *We're studying the geography of Asia.*

glasses (n) ○━ /'glɑːsɪz/ people wear these to be able to see better or protect their eyes form bright sunlight: *My sister wears glasses for reading.*

green (adj) ○━ /griːn/ having the colour of grass and leaves: *My cat has got green eyes.*

grey (adj) ○━ /greɪ/ the colour between black and white: *My father's hair is going grey.*

heavy (adj) ○━ /'hevi/ weighing a lot: *I'm too heavy; I need to do more exercise.*

history (n) ○━ /'hɪstri/ the study of past events: *My brother is really interested in the history of the two World Wars.*

how (adv) ○━ /haʊ/: *How old are you?*

ICT (Information and Communication Technology) (n) /ˌaɪ ˌsiː 'tiː, ˌɪnfəˌmeɪʃn ən kəmjuːnɪˌkeɪʃn ˌtek'nɒlədʒi/ the study of computers and digital communication: *We're learning to build a website in ICT.*

in (prep) ○━ /ɪn/ inside: *She put her keys in her bag.*

in front of (prep) ○━ /ˌɪn 'frʌnt əv/ in a position further forward than but close to somebody or something: *The bus stops right in front of our house.*

lamp (n) ○━ /læmp/ a device in the home that uses electricity to produce light: *I have a lamp by my bed so that I can read before I go to sleep.*

long (adj) ○━ /lɒŋ/ measuring a great amount: *She has really long hair, almost down to her waist.*

maths (n) ○━ /mæθs/ the study of numbers, quantities or shapes: *Maths was my favourite subject at school.*

medium-length (adj) /'miːdiəm ˌleŋθ/ (of hair) reaching to the shoulders: *Her hair used to be short but now it's medium-length.*

microwave (n) /'maɪkrəweɪv/ a type of oven that cooks or heats food very quickly: *Let's heat this soup in the microwave.*

mirror (n) ○━ /'mɪrə(r)/ a piece of special glass that you can look into in order to see yourself: *There's a big mirror in the bathroom.*

moustache (n) ○━ /mə'stɑːʃ/ hair that grows on the top lip, between the mouth and the nose: *Has he got a moustache?*

near (prep) ○━ /nɪə(r)/ not far way: *Let's walk to the library; it's quite near.*

next to (prep) ○━ /'neks ˌtuː, tə/ at the side of somebody or something: *There's a book shop next to the museum.*

on (prep) ○━ /ɒn/ supported by, fixed to or touching something: *We sat on the floor.*

PE (physical education) (n) ○━ /ˌpiː 'iː, ˌfɪzɪkl edʒu'keɪʃn/ the instruction in sports, physical exercise and hygiene: *We do all our PE classes outside unless the weather is really bad.*

/i/ happy	/æ/ flag	/ɜː/ her	/ʊ/ look	/ʌ/ mum	/ɔɪ/ noisy	/ɪə/ here
/ɪ/ it	/ɑː/ art	/ɒ/ not	/uː/ you	/eɪ/ day	/aʊ/ how	/eə/ wear
/iː/ he	/e/ egg	/ɔː/ four	/ə/ sugar	/aɪ/ why	/əʊ/ go	/ʊə/ tourist

physics (n) 🔊 /ˈfɪzɪks/ the scientific study of natural forces such as light, sound, heat, etc.: *We are learning about the speed of sound in physics.*

picture (n) 🔊 /ˈpɪktʃə(r)/ a painting, drawing or photograph: *Who painted the picture in the hall?*

quite (adv) 🔊 /kwaɪt/ not very: *She's quite tall for her age.*

RE (religious education) (n) 🔊 /ɑːr iː, rɪˌlɪdʒəs ˈstʌdiz/ the study of different religions: *We've been learning about the Hindu beliefs of creation and evolution in religious education.*

short (adj) 🔊 /ʃɔːt/ not measuring much from one end to the other; opposite of long or tall: *Boys have to have short hair in our school.*

social studies (n) 🔊 /ˌsəʊʃl ˈstʌdiz/ the study of aspects of human society: *We learn about other people and their values in social studies.*

sofa (n) /ˈsəʊfə/ a soft comfortable seat with a back for two or more people to sit on: *We have a leather sofa in the living room.*

straight (adj) 🔊 /streɪt/ (of hair) not curly: *My hair is curly but I'd prefer straight hair.*

strange (adj) 🔊 /streɪndʒ/ unusual or surprising: *A strange thing happened this morning.*

table (n) 🔊 /ˈteɪbl/ a piece of furniture with a flat top supported by legs: *Could you lay the table for lunch, please?*

tall (adj) 🔊 /tɔːl/ (used about people) of more than average height: *All the players in our basketball team are extremely tall.*

TV (television) (n) 🔊 /ˌtiː ˈviː (ˈteləvɪʒn)/ a piece of electrical equipment with a glass screen which shows programmes with moving pictures and sounds: *Are there any good films on TV this evening?*

under (prep) 🔊 /ˈʌndə(r)/ in or to a position that is below something: *We found him hiding under the table.*

wardrobe (n) 🔊 /ˈwɔːdrəʊb/ a large cupboard in which you can hang your clothes: *Please hang your new dress in your wardrobe.*

washing machine (n) 🔊 /ˈwɒʃɪŋ məˌʃiːn/ an electric machine for washing clothes: *Put your dirty football kit in the washing machine.*

wavy (adj) 🔊 /ˈweɪvi/ (of hair) having some curls: *He's got short, wavy hair.*

what (pron) 🔊 /wɒt/: *What is your name?*

when (adv) 🔊 /wen/: *When is your birthday?*

where (adv) 🔊 /weə(r)/: *Where do you live?*

which (pron) 🔊 /wɪtʃ/: *Which two colours make green?*

who (pron) 🔊 /huː/: *Who is your English teacher?*

why (adv) 🔊 /waɪ/: *Why don't you like ice cream?*

UNIT 1

American (adj) /əˈmerɪkən/

Bahraini (adj) /bɑːˈreɪni/

British (adj) /ˈbrɪtɪʃ/

capital city (n) 🔊 /ˌkæpɪtl ˈsɪti/ the town or city where the government of a country is: *Tokyo is the capital of Japan.*

Chinese (adj) /tʃaɪˈniːz/

climate (n) 🔊 /ˈklaɪmət/ the normal weather conditions of a particular region: *Saudi Arabia has a desert climate.*

cosmopolitan (adj) /kɒzməˈpɒlɪtən/

culture (n) 🔊 /ˈkʌltʃə(r)/

currency (n) /ˈkʌrənsi/ the system or type of money a particular country uses: *The currency in the UK is the British pound.*

deli / delicatessen (n) /ˈdeli, delɪkəˈtesn/

do exercise (verb phrase) 🔊 /ˌduː ˈeksəsaɪz/ to do a physical activity to make you strong and healthy: *The students do exercise after school.*

Egyptian (adj) /iˈdʒɪpʃn/

English (adj) /ˈɪŋglɪʃ/

export (n) 🔊 /ˈekspɔːt/ something that is sent to another country for sale: *Coffee is one of Brazil's main exports.*

feed the animals (verb phrase) 🔊 /ˌfiːd ðiː ˈænɪmlz/ to give food to an animal: *The farmer feeds his animals in the winter.*

fetch water (verb phrase) 🔊 /ˌfetʃ ˈwɔːtə(r)/ to go for and bring back water: *There is no tap in the village, so Amber fetches water from the river.*

finish school (verb phrase) 🔊 /ˌfɪnɪʃ ˈskuːl/ the time classes end: *We finish school at 3.30 p.m.*

French (adj) /frentʃ/

German (adj) /ˈdʒɜːmən/

go to sleep (verb phrase) 🔊 /ˌgəʊ tə ˈsliːp/ to fall asleep: *On a school night, Liz goes to sleep at about 9.30 p.m.*

hang out (with) (verb phrase) 🔊 /ˌhæŋ ˈaʊt (ˌwɪð)/ to spend time relaxing: *Many teenagers like to hang out at the mall after school.*

have a break (verb phrase) 🔊 /ˌhæv ə ˈbreɪk/ to stop working and rest: *Students have a break at lunchtime for 45 minutes.*

have dinner (verb phrase) 🔊 /ˌhæv ˈdɪnə(r)/ to eat your evening meal: *We have dinner with the whole family every evening.*

Lebanese (adj) /lebəˈniːz/

mix (v) 🔊 /mɪks/

Moroccan (adj) /məˈrɒkən/

national sport (n) 🔊 /ˌnæʃnəl ˈspɔːt/ the sport connected with the culture of a country: *Ice hockey is a Canadian national sport.*

nationality (n) /næʃəˈnæləti/ the state of being legally a citizen of a particular nation or country: *Rob lives in America, but he still has French nationality.*

official language (n) 🔊 /əˈfɪʃl ˌlæŋgwɪdʒ/ the language that is accepted by a country's government, is taught in schools, etc.: *The official language of China is standard Mandarin.*

originally (adv) 🔊 /əˈrɪdʒənəli/

Polish (adj) 🔊 /ˈpəʊlɪʃ/

population (n) 🔊 /pɒpjuˈleɪʃn/ the number of people who live in an area, city or country: *A megacity is any city with a population higher than 10 million people.*

race (n) 🔊 /reɪs/

reputation (n) 🔊 /repjuˈteɪʃn/

say your prayers (verb phrase) 🔊 /ˌseɪ jɔː ˈpreəz/ to give thanks or ask for help to a deity: *Rashid says his prayers every night before he goes to bed.*

Spanish (adj) /ˈspænɪʃ/

Turkish (adj) /ˈtɜːkɪʃ/

wake up (verb phrase) 🔊 /ˌweɪk ˈʌp/ to stop sleeping: *I usually wake up at 7.00 a.m.*

Yemeni (adj) /ˈjeməni/

/p/ pen	/d/ dog	/tʃ/ beach	/v/ very	/s/ speak	/ʒ/ television	/n/ now	/r/ radio
/b/ big	/k/ can	/dʒ/ job	/θ/ think	/z/ zoo	/h/ house	/ŋ/ sing	/j/ yes
/t/ two	/g/ good	/f/ food	/ð/ then	/ʃ/ she	/m/ meat	/l/ late	/w/ we

Words to learn

background (n) 🔊 /'bækgraʊnd/

bake cakes (verb phrase) 🔊 /,beɪk 'keɪks/ to make cakes in an oven: *Laila is baking cakes for the picnic.*

clear the table (verb phrase) 🔊 /,klɪə ðə 'teɪbl/ to remove dishes and cutlery from the table after eating: *I prefer to clear the table after a meal to doing the washing-up.*

collect coins (verb phrase) 🔊 /kə,lekt 'kɔɪnz/ to look for and buy old coins for a collection: *My uncle likes to collect coins from around the world.*

do the vacuuming (verb phrase) 🔊 /,duː ðə 'vækjuəmɪŋ/ to clean the floors and carpets using a vacuum cleaner: *We don't have a vacuum cleaner so no one does the vacuuming in our house.*

do the washing-up (verb phrase) 🔊 /,duː ðə ,wɒʃɪŋ 'ʌp/ to wash the dishes after a meal: *We don't often do the washing-up because we have a dishwasher.*

full-time (adj) /'fʊl ,taɪm/

gather (v) 🔊 /'gæðə(r)/

generation (n) 🔊 /dʒenə'reɪʃn/

go deep-sea fishing (verb phrase) /,gəʊ ,diːp ,siː 'fɪʃɪŋ/ to catch fish from a boat: *We went deep-sea fishing on holiday.*

go online (verb phrase) 🔊 /,gəʊ ɒn'laɪn/ to connect to the internet: *Yusuf went online to do research for his project.*

go to the gym (verb phrase) /,gəʊ tə ðə 'dʒɪm/ to do exercise in a gymnasium: *Sarah likes to keep fit so she goes to the gym three times a week.*

household (n) 🔊 /'haʊshəʊld/

load the dishwasher (verb phrase) /,ləʊd ðə 'dɪʃwɒʃə(r)/ to put dirty plates and cutlery in the dishwasher for cleaning: *My brother loads the dishwasher with the dirty plates after dinner.*

make a video (verb phrase) 🔊 /,meɪk ə 'vɪdiəʊ/ to record an event using a video camera: *We made a video about our holiday to New York.*

make dinner (verb phrase) 🔊 /,meɪk 'dɪnə(r)/ to cook the evening meal: *Mum makes dinner every evening. She's a great cook.*

make your bed (verb phrase) 🔊 /,meɪk ,jɔː 'bed/ to arrange the sheets on your bed: *I make my bed every morning as soon as I get up.*

only child (n) 🔊 /,əʊnli 'tʃaɪld/

orphan (n) /'ɔːfn/

play golf (verb phrase) /,pleɪ 'gɒlf/ a game that is played outdoors on a large area of grass: *Do you enjoy playing golf?*

put away your clothes (verb phrase) 🔊 /,pʊt ə,weɪ ,jɔː 'kləʊðz/ to put your clothes in your wardrobe: *My mum does the washing and then I put the clothes away.*

sibling (n) /'sɪblɪŋ/

take out the rubbish (verb phrase) 🔊 /,teɪk ,aʊt ðə 'rʌbɪʃ/ to carry the rubbish to the bin outside the home: *My dad takes out the rubbish when the bin is full.*

tidy up your room (verb phrase) 🔊 /,taɪdi ,ʌp ,jɔː 'ruːm/ to arrange the things in your bedroom: *I share a bedroom with my sister. We take it in turns to tidy up when it gets messy.*

undo (v) 🔊 /ʌn'duː/

unfold (v) 🔊 /ʌn'fəʊld/

unload (v) 🔊 /ʌn'ləʊd/

unlock (v) /ʌn'lɒk/

unpack the shopping (verb phrase) /ʌn,pæk ðə 'ʃɒpɪŋ/ to remove the contents of a shopping bag and put them in the kitchen cupboards and fridge: *I like to unpack the shopping after Mum has been to the supermarket so that I can see what food she has bought.*

unplug (v) /ʌn'plʌg/

unwrap (v) /ʌn'ræp/

write a blog (verb phrase) /,raɪt ə 'blɒg/ to write material (e.g. opinions, information, a diary) for a personal website: *Jamal writes a blog about all the books he reads.*

adventurous (adj) /əd'ventʃərəs/

backpack (v) /'bækpæk/ to go on holiday with your clothes, etc. in a backpack: *We went backpacking round Europe last summer.*

buy souvenirs (v) /,baɪ suːvə'nɪəz/ to buy things to remind you of somewhere you have been on holiday: *I buy souvenirs every time I go on holiday.*

canal (n) /kə'næl/ a deep cut that is made through the land so that boats or ships can travel along it: *The Panama Canal connects the Atlantic to the Pacific Ocean.*

canyon (n) /'kænjən/ a deep valley with very steep sides: *The Colorado River runs through the Grand Canyon.*

challenging (adj) 🔊 /'tʃælɪndʒɪŋ/

charity (n) 🔊 /'tʃærəti/

chill out (v) /,tʃɪl 'aʊt/ to relax: *There's nothing better than chilling out by the pool in the summer.*

desert (n) 🔊 /'dezət/ a large area of land, usually covered in sand that is hot and has very little water and very few plants: *The Atacama Desert in South America is the driest place in the world.*

do a course (verb phrase) 🔊 /,duː ə 'kɔːs/

do nothing (verb phrase) 🔊 /,duː 'nʌθɪŋ/

do research (verb phrase) 🔊 /,duː rɪ'sɜːtʃ, 'riːsɜːtʃ/

eat out (v) 🔊 /,iːt 'aʊt/ to eat a meal in a restaurant: *We ate out almost every night when we went to Tunisia.*

expedition (n) /ekspə'dɪʃn/

falls (n) 🔊 /fɔːlz/ a large amount of water that falls from a height down the side of a mountain, also called a waterfall: *Three waterfalls (Horseshoe, American and Bridal Veil Falls) make up Niagara Falls.*

impressive (adj) 🔊 /ɪm'presɪv/

in aid of (noun phrase) 🔊 /ɪn 'eɪd əv/

lake (n) 🔊 /leɪk/ a large area of water that is surrounded by land: *They've gone sailing on the lake.*

make a list (verb phrase) 🔊 /,meɪk ə 'lɪst/

make a noise (verb phrase) 🔊 /,meɪk ə 'nɔɪz/

make plans (verb phrase) 🔊 /,meɪk 'plænz/

memorable (adj) /'memərəbl/

monitor (v) 🔊 /'mɒnɪtə(r)/

mountain (n) 🔊 /'maʊntən/ a very high hill: *Everest is the highest mountain the world.*

ocean (n) 🔊 /'əʊʃn/ the mass of salt water that covers most of the surface of the Earth: *Two thirds of the Earth's surface is covered by ocean.*

original (adj) 🔊 /ə'rɪdʒənl/

/i/ happy	/æ/ flag	/ɜː/ her	/ʊ/ look	/ʌ/ mum	/ɔɪ/ noisy	/ɪə/ here
/ɪ/ it	/ɑː/ art	/ɒ/ not	/uː/ you	/eɪ/ day	/aʊ/ how	/eə/ wear
/iː/ he	/e/ egg	/ɔː/ four	/ə/ sugar	/aɪ/ why	/əʊ/ go	/ʊə/ tourist

pole (n) 0ㅡ /pəʊl/ either of the two points at the exact top and bottom of the Earth: *At the North Pole, all directions point south.*

rainforest (n) /'reɪnfɒrɪst/ a thick forest in tropical parts of the world that have a lot of rain: *Global warming could lead to a shift in weather patterns that would cause the Amazon rainforest to dry up and die in 50 years.*

river (n) 0ㅡ /'rɪvə(r)/ a large natural flow of water that goes across land and into the sea: *Tom sat down on the bank of the river to fish.*

scuba dive (v) /'skuːbə ˌdaɪv/ to swim under water using special equipment for breathing: *A great place to go scuba diving is the Red Sea.*

sea (n) 0ㅡ /siː/ a particular large area of salt water – it may be part of the ocean or it may be surrounded by land: *Many people like to go scuba diving in the Red Sea.*

sightsee (v) /'saɪtsiː/ to visit the sights of a city: *We went sightseeing every day when we visited Rome.*

spectacular (adj) /spek'tækjələ(r)/

sponsor (v) /'spɒnsə(r)/

survey (n) 0ㅡ /'sɜːveɪ/

trek (v) /trek/ to go on a long, hard walk: *I'd like to go trekking across a desert with camels.*

unspoilt (adj) /ʌn'spɔɪlt/

valley (n) 0ㅡ /'væli/ the low land between two mountains, which often has a river flowing through it: *Death Valley is the hottest place in the world.*

visit relatives (v) 0ㅡ /ˌvɪzɪt 'relətɪvz/ to visit members of your family: *We usually visit relatives at the weekend.*

UNIT 4 ▮▮▮▯

according to (prepositional phrase) 0ㅡ /ə'kɔːdɪŋ tə/

addiction (n) /ə'dɪkʃn/

average (n) 0ㅡ /'ævərɪdʒ/

awful (adj) 0ㅡ /'ɔːfl/

baked potato (n) 0ㅡ /ˌbeɪkt pə'teɪtəʊ/ a potato that has been cooked in an oven: *A baked potato with butter and topped with grated cheese is a family favourite.*

calorie (n) /'kæləri/ a unit for measuring how much energy food will produce: *A fried egg contains about 100 calories.*

carbohydrate (n) /kɑːbəʊ'haɪdreɪt/ one of the substances in food, for example sugar, that gives you're body energy: *Athletes need a diet that is high in carbohydrate.*

chocolate muffin (n) /ˌtʃɒklət 'mʌfɪn/ a small domed spongy cake with a chocolate flavour: *I have a chocolate muffin and a coffee for breakfast every Sunday.*

documentary (n) /dɒkju'mentri/

energy (n) 0ㅡ /'enədʒi/

exhausted (adj) /ɪg'zɔːstɪd/

experiment (n) 0ㅡ /ɪk'sperɪmənt/

fascinating (adj) /'fæsɪneɪtɪŋ/

fattening (adj) /'fætnɪŋ/ (used about food) that makes the body fat: *Chocolate is very fattening.*

fit (adj) 0ㅡ /fɪt/ strong and in good physical health: *Swimming is a good way to keep fit.*

fried rice (n) 0ㅡ /ˌfraɪd 'raɪs/ a dish of steamed rice that has been stir-fried in a wok: *Many Chinese restaurants serve fried rice with their dishes.*

fruit smoothie (n) /ˌfruːt 'smuːði/ a thick, smooth drink of fresh fruit that has been mixed with milk, yoghurt or ice cream: *Some fruit smoothies have more sugar in them than a fizzy drink.*

huge (adj) 0ㅡ /hjuːdʒ/

in a bad mood (noun phrase) 0ㅡ /ˌɪn ə ˌbæd 'muːd/

in their opinion (prepositional phrase) 0ㅡ /ɪn 'ðeər ə,pɪnjən/

instead of (prepositional phrase) 0ㅡ /ɪn'sted əv/

junk food (n) /'dʒʌŋk ˌfuːd/

lack of (prepositional phrase) 0ㅡ /'læk əv/

mineral water (n) 0ㅡ /'mɪnərəl ˌwɔːtə(r)/ water occurring naturally containing some dissolved salts, sold as drinking water: *In some shops, mineral water is more expensive than petrol.*

nutritious (adj) /nju'trɪʃəs/ (used about food) very good for you: *Home cooked food is much more nutritious than ready-made meals.*

on average (prepositional phrase) d /ˌɒn 'ævərɪdʒ/

overweight (adj) /ˌəʊvə'weɪt/ too heavy or fat: *I'm a bit overweight – I think I might go on a diet.*

protein (n) /'prəʊtiːn/ a substance in food such as meat, fish, eggs and beans that people need in order to grow and be healthy: *Weight lifters need a lot of protein in their diet.*

salty (adj) 0ㅡ /'sɔːlti/ having the taste of or containing salt: *I didn't like the meat; it was too salty.*

starving (adj) /'stɑːvɪŋ/

sugar (n) 0ㅡ /'ʃʊgə(r)/ a sweet substance that you get from certain plants: *A lot of low fat foods contain high amounts of sugar, which means that they are still fattening.*

tomato salad (n) 0ㅡ /təˌmɑːtəʊ 'sæləd/ a salad made primarily of tomatoes: *A tomato salad is very easy to prepare.*

tuna wrap (n) /ˌtjuːnə 'ræp/ creamed tuna with salad and grated cheese wrapped in a tortilla: *Tuna wraps are a quick and easy meal to make for lunch.*

vegetable soup (n) 0ㅡ /ˌvedʒtəbl 'suːp/ soup made of chopped vegetables: *Vegetable soup is a cheap and nutritious meal to make.*

vitamin (n) /'vɪtəmɪn/ one of several substances that are found in certain types of food and that are important for growth and good health: *Oranges are rich in vitamin C.*

UNIT 5 ▮▮▮▯

amazed (adj) 0ㅡ /ə'meɪzd/ very surprised: *I was amazed that he passed the exam so easily.*

amazing (adj) 0ㅡ /ə'meɪzɪŋ/

amused (adj) 0ㅡ /ə'mjuːzd/ very funny: *I was amused to hear his version of what happened.*

amusing (adj) 0ㅡ /ə'mjuːzɪŋ/

annoyed (adj) 0ㅡ /ə'nɔɪd/ feeling angry or slightly angry: *I will be extremely annoyed if Talib is late again.*

annoying (adj) 0ㅡ /ə'nɔɪɪŋ/

be born (verb phrase) 0ㅡ /ˌbi 'bɔːn/: *My father was born in Hong Kong.*

become rich (verb phrase) 0ㅡ /bɪˌkʌm 'rɪtʃ/: *Nasir became very rich when he sold his company.*

bored (adj) 0ㅡ /bɔːd/ feeling tired and slightly annoyed because something isn't interesting: *Small children often get*

/p/ pen	/d/ dog	/tʃ/ beach	/v/ very	/s/ speak	/ʒ/ television	/n/ now	/r/ radio
/b/ big	/k/ can	/dʒ/ job	/θ/ think	/z/ zoo	/h/ house	/ŋ/ sing	/j/ yes
/t/ two	/g/ good	/f/ food	/ð/ then	/ʃ/ she	/m/ meat	/l/ late	/w/ we

Words to learn

bored on long car journeys.

boring (adj) 🔊 /'bɔːrɪŋ/

buy a house (verb phrase) 🔊 /ˌbaɪ ə 'haʊs/: *I'll buy a house when I get a good job.*

confused (adj) 🔊 /kənˈfjuːzd/ not able to understand or think clearly: *I was still confused after Hassan tried to explain the maths homework for the second time.*

confusing (adj) 🔊 /kənˈfjuːzɪŋ/

detailed (adj) 🔊 /ˈdiːteɪld/

digit (n) /ˈdɪdʒɪt/

disappointed (adj) 🔊 /dɪsəˈpɔɪntɪd/ sad because something did not succeed or wasn't as good / interesting, etc. as you had hoped: *Lana was disappointed she wasn't chosen for the team.*

disappointing (adj) 🔊 /dɪsəˈpɔɪntɪŋ/

embarrassed (adj) 🔊 /ɪmˈbærəst/ feeling uncomfortable or shy because of something silly you have done: *I felt so embarrassed when I dropped my glass.*

embarrassing (adj) 🔊 /ɪmˈbærəsɪŋ/

excited (adj) 🔊 /ɪkˈsaɪtɪd/ feeling or showing happiness and enthusiasm: *Are you getting excited about your holiday?*

exciting (adj) 🔊 /ɪkˈsaɪtɪŋ/

get a job (verb phrase) 🔊 /ˌget ə 'dʒɒb/: *I'd like to get a job in journalism.*

get married (verb phrase) 🔊 /ˌget 'mærid/: *You can get married in the UK if you are over 16 years old.*

graduate from university (verb phrase) 🔊 /ˌgrædjueɪt frəm junɪˈvɜːsəti/: *My brother graduated from university with a degree in medicine.*

have a child (verb phrase) 🔊 /ˌhæv ə 'tʃaɪld/: *In your opinion, what is the best age to have a child?*

interested (adj) 🔊 /ˈɪntrəstɪd/

learn to drive (verb phrase) 🔊 /ˌlɜːn tə 'draɪv/: *My grandmother never learnt to drive, so she goes everywhere by bus.*

leave school (verb phrase) 🔊 /ˌliːv 'skuːl/: *When I leave school, I'll go to university.*

maximum (adj) 🔊 /ˈmæksɪməm/

memorise (v) /ˈmeməraɪz/

move to another country (verb phrase) 🔊 /ˌmuːv tuː əˌnʌðə ˈkʌntri/: *Would you move to another country to get a better job?*

personal (adj) 🔊 /ˈpɜːsənl/

photographic (adj) /fəʊtəˈgræfɪk/

photographic memory (n) /fəʊtəˌgræfɪk ˈmeməri/

pi (n) /paɪ/

recite (verb) /rɪˈsaɪt/

record (n) 🔊 /ˈrekɔːd/

satisfied (adj) 🔊 /ˈsætɪsfaɪd/ pleased because you have achieved something or because something that you wanted to happen has happened: *He had a satisfied smile on his face when he finished all his homework for the week.*

satisfying (adj) 🔊 /ˈsætɪsfaɪɪŋ/

start a company (verb phrase) d /ˌstɑːt ə 'kʌmpəni/: *If you want to be your own boss, you need to start a company.*

surprised (adj) 🔊 /səˈpraɪzd/ feeling or showing surprise: *I was very surprised to see Cathy at the cinema. I thought she was still on holiday.*

surprising (adj) 🔊 /səˈpraɪzɪŋ/

technique (n) 🔊 /tekˈniːk/

UNIT 6

across (prep) 🔊 /əˈkrɒs/ from one side of something to the other: *He walked across the field.*

along (prep) 🔊 /əˈlɒŋ/ from one end to or towards the other end of something: *Aziz walked slowly along the road.*

around (prep) 🔊 /əˈraʊnd/ forming a circle: *Maya cycled around the lake.*

barrel (n) /ˈbærəl/

border (n) 🔊 /ˈbɔːdə(r)/

bungee jumping (n) /ˈbʌndʒi ˌdʒʌmpɪŋ/ a sport in which you jump from a high place with a thick elastic tied round your feet: *The Kawarau Bridge in New Zealand is a popular place to go bungee jumping.*

cave diving (noun) /ˈkeɪv ˌdaɪvɪŋ/ underwater diving in caves: *Cave diving can be quite dangerous.*

daring (adj) 🔊 /ˈdeərɪŋ/

down (prep) 🔊 /daʊn/ to a lower level or place: *Skiing down a steep mountain is dangerous.*

every hour (time expression) 🔊 /ˌevri ˈaʊə(r)/

fine (n) 🔊 /faɪn/

for (40) minutes (time expression) 🔊 /fə ˌ(...) 'mɪnɪts/

hang-gliding (n) /ˈhæŋ ˌglaɪdɪŋ/ a sport in which you fly through the air holding onto a type of frame covered in cloth: *My grandfather first went hang-gliding at the age of 55.*

hero (n) 🔊 /ˈhɪərəʊ/

heroine (n) /ˈherəʊɪn/

ice climbing (n) 🔊 /ˈaɪs ˌklaɪmɪŋ/ the sport of climbing glaciers: *Ice climbing is a popular sport in Iceland.*

in (1860) (time expression) 🔊 /ɪn/

in the past (time expression) 🔊 /ˌɪn ðə 'pɑːst/

into (prep) 🔊 /ˈɪntuː, ˈɪntə/ moving to a position inside or in something: *Karen and Tanya dived into the swimming pool.*

kitesurfing (n) /ˈkaɪtsɜːfɪŋ/ a sport in which you ride a modified surfboard while holding onto a specially-designed kite, using the wind for propulsion: *You have to be a good swimmer to go kite-surfing as you'll fall into the sea a lot.*

off (prep) 🔊 /ɒf/ down or away from a place or a position on something: *We got off the bus at the post office.*

out of (prep) 🔊 /ˈaʊt əv/ away from the inside of a place: *He swam to the edge and got out of the pool.*

prohibited (adj) /prəˈhɪbɪtɪd/

sandboarding (n) /ˈsændbɔːdɪŋ/ a board sport similar to snowboarding that takes place on sand dunes: *Sandboarding is like snowboarding but you do it in the desert.*

stunt artist (n) /ˈstʌnt ˌɑːtɪst/

that day (time expression) 🔊 /ˈðæt ˌdeɪ/

these days (time expression) 🔊 /ˈðiːz ˌdeɪz/

through (prep) 🔊 /θruː/ from one or side of something to the other: *We drove through the desert.*

tightrope (n) /ˈtaɪtrəʊp/

under (prep) 🔊 /ˈʌndə(r)/ to a position that is below something: *The helicopter flew under the bridge.*

up (prep) 🔊 /ʌp/ to a higher level or position: *The stunt artist climbed up the building.*

white-water rafting (n) /ˌwaɪt ˌwɔːtə 'rɑːftɪŋ/ the sport of navigating rough water using an inflatable raft: *I fell out of the boat when I was white-water rafting.*

/i/ happy	/æ/ flag	/ɜː/ her	/ʊ/ look	/ʌ/ mum	/ɔɪ/ noisy	/ɪə/ here
/ɪ/ it	/ɑː/ art	/ɒ/ not	/uː/ you	/eɪ/ day	/aʊ/ how	/eə/ wear
/iː/ he	/e/ egg	/ɔː/ four	/ə/ sugar	/aɪ/ why	/əʊ/ go	/ʊə/ tourist

wingsuit flying (n) /ˈwɪŋsuːt ˌflaɪɪŋ/ flying through the air wearing a special suit that adds surface area to the body to create lift: *Some adventurers climb to the top of a high cliff, then come back down by wingsuit flying.*

UNIT 7

accountant (n) /əˈkaʊntənt/ a person whose job is to keep or examine the financial accounts of a business: *He's an accountant in a large firm in the city.*

ambitious (adj) /æmˈbɪʃəs/

architect (n) /ˈɑːkɪtekt/ a person whose job is to design buildings: *Who was the architect who designed the Burj Al Arab hotel?*

by accident (prepositional phrase) /baɪ ˈæksɪdənt/

by any chance (prepositional phrase) /ˌbaɪ ˈeni ˌtʃɑːns/

by hand (prepositional phrase) /ˌbaɪ ˈhænd/

by heart (prepositional phrase) /ˌbaɪ ˈhɑːt/

by law (prepositional phrase) /ˌbaɪ ˈlɔː/

by yourself (prepositional phrase) /ˌbaɪ jɔːˈself/

clearly (adv) /ˈklɪəli/

compose (v) /kəmˈpəʊz/ to write music: *We're going to compose some music for the school concert.*

composer (n) /kəmˈpəʊzə(r)/ a person who writes music: *That music is by a composer called Chopin.*

design (v) /dɪˈzaɪn/ to invent, plan and develop something for a particular purpose: *He's decided to design his own company logo.*

designer (n) /dɪˈzaɪnə(r)/ a person whose job is to show how something will be made: *Samir is a website designer.*

electrician (n) /ɪlekˈtrɪʃn/ a person whose job is make and repair electrical systems: *We need an electrician to install our security lights.*

encourage (v) /ɪnˈkʌrɪdʒ/

fashion designer (n) /ˈfæʃn dɪˌzaɪnə(r)/ a person whose job is to design fashionable clothes: *All the famous fashion designers seem to be Italian or French.*

fluently (adv) /ˈfluːəntli/

fortunately (adv) /ˈfɔːtʃənətli/

genius (n) /ˈdʒiːniəs/

invent (v) /ɪnˈvent/ to think of or make something for the first time: *Did Edison invent the light bulb?*

inventor (n) /ɪnˈventə(r)/ a person who invents something for the first time: *Alexander Graham Bell is the inventor of the telephone.*

IQ (n) /ˌaɪ ˈkjuː/

lawyer (n) /ˈlɔːjə(r)/ a person who has a certificate in law: *Max works in the legal system; he's a lawyer.*

librarian (n) /laɪˈbreəriən/ a person who works in or is in charge of a library: *The school librarian helped me find some useful information for my school project.*

mechanic (n) /məˈkænɪk/ a person whose job is to repair and work with machines: *Sami can fix your car; he's a mechanic.*

nurse (n) /nɜːs/ a person who is trained to look after sick or injured people: *My neighbour is a psychiatric nurse.*

paint (v) /peɪnt/ to put paint onto something: *When did Picasso paint Le Picador?*

painter (n) /ˈpeɪntə(r)/ a person who paints: *How many American painters can you name?*

program (n) /ˈprəʊgræm/ a set of instructions that you give to a computer so that it will carry out a particular task: *Have you ever written a computer program?*

programmer (n) /ˈprəʊgræmə(r)/ a person whose job is to write programs for a computer: *I'd like to be a computer programmer.*

push (v) /pʊʃ/

sadly (adv) /ˈsædli/

software developer (n) /ˈsɒftweə dɪˌveləpə(r)/ a person whose job is to write programs and other operating information used by a computer: *Software developers make computer programs to help people.*

strict (adj) /strɪkt/

talented (adj) /ˈtæləntɪd/

tour guide (n) /ˈtʊə ˌgaɪd/ a person whose job is to organise tours and provide cultural and historical information on the tour: *Our tour guide told us lots of interesting facts about the history of the area.*

unfortunately (adv) /ʌnˈfɔːtʃənətli/

write (v) /raɪt/ to make words, letters, etc.: *Amira wants to write a novel.*

writer (n) /ˈraɪtə(r)/ a person who writes, especially one whose job is to write books, stories, etc.: *The Brontë sisters were writers.*

UNIT 8

billion (n) /ˈbɪljən/

car park (n) /ˈkɑː ˌpɑːk/ an area or a building where you can leave your car: *Can you remember where in the car park you left the car?*

century (n) /ˈsentʃəri/

clean (adj) /kliːn/ not dirty: *There are no cars in Masdar, so it's a very clean city.*

couple (number) /ˈkʌpl/

crowded (adj) /ˈkraʊdɪd/ full of people

day (n) /deɪ/

decade (n) /ˈdekeɪd/

deserted (adj) /dɪˈzɜːtɪd/ empty, because all the people have left: *It was so early, the streets were deserted.*

dozen (number) /ˈdʌzn/

environmentally friendly (adj) /ɪnvaɪrənˌmentəli ˈfrendli/

few (number) /fjuː/

flat (adj) /flæt/ smooth and level, with no parts that are higher than the rest: *The countryside round here is very flat.*

green space (n) /ˌgriːn ˈspeɪs/ an area of grass, trees, etc. in an otherwise urban environment: *The main green space in New York is Central Park.*

high-rise building (n) /ˈhaɪ ˌraɪz ˌbɪldɪŋ/ a very tall building with lots of floors: *There are lots of high-rise buildings in Tokyo.*

hilly (adj) /ˈhɪli/ having lots of hills: *Scotland is quite a hilly country.*

historic (adj) /hɪˈstɒrɪk/ famous or important in history: *The area is of special historic interest.*

hour (n) /ˈaʊə(r)/

hundred (number) /ˈhʌndrəd/

/p/ pen	/d/ dog	/tʃ/ beach	/v/ very	/s/ speak	/ʒ/ television	/n/ now	/r/ radio
/b/ big	/k/ can	/dʒ/ job	/θ/ think	/z/ zoo	/h/ house	/ŋ/ sing	/j/ yes
/t/ two	/g/ good	/f/ food	/ð/ then	/ʃ/ she	/m/ meat	/l/ late	/w/ we

main road (n) 🔊 /ˌmeɪn ˈrəʊd/ a major road for any form of motor transport: *The main road through town is always very busy with cars and lorries.*

migrate (v) /maɪˈɡreɪt/

millennium (n) /mɪˈleniəm/

million (number) 🔊 /ˈmɪljən/

minute (n) 🔊 /ˈmɪnɪt/

modern (adj) 🔊 /ˈmɒdn/ of the present or recent times: *Pollution is one of the major problems of the modern world.*

month (n) 🔊 /mʌnθ/

nought (number) 🔊 /nɔːt/

overpopulation (n) /ˌəʊvəpɒpjuˈleɪʃn/

pedestrian crossing (n) /pəˌdestriən ˈkrɒsɪŋ/ a place for people to cross the road: *The safest place to cross the road is at the pedestrian crossing.*

petrol station (n) 🔊 /ˈpetrəl ˌsteɪʃn/ a place where you can buy petrol and other things for your car: *Let's stop at the petrol station for petrol and water before we drive to London.*

polluted (adj) 🔊 /pəˈluːtɪd/ where the air, water, etc. has been made dirty and dangerous: *The beach is polluted with oil.*

pollution (n) 🔊 /pəˈluːʃn/

quarter (number) 🔊 /ˈkwɔːtə(r)/

renewable energy (n) /rɪˌnjuːəbl ˈenədʒi/

retail park (n) /ˈriːteɪl ˌpɑːk/ a shopping development outside a city that contains a (number) of large chain stores: *I prefer to go shopping at retail parks as all the big shops are close together.*

rural (adj) 🔊 /ˈrʊərəl/ connected with the countryside

second (n) 🔊 /ˈsekənd/

shortage (n) /ˈʃɔːtɪdʒ/

skyscraper (n) /ˈskaɪskreɪpə(r)/

thousand (number) 🔊 /ˈθaʊznd/

traffic lights (n) 🔊 /ˈtræfɪk ˌlaɪts/ a sign with three coloured lights (red, amber and green) that is used for controlling the traffic where two or more roads meet: *Get ready to go when the light turns amber.*

trend (n) 🔊 /trend/

urban (adj) 🔊 /ˈɜːbən/ connected with a town or city

week (n) 🔊 /wiːk/

year (n) 🔊 /jɪə(r)/

◖ UNIT 9 ▮▮ ▮ ▮ ▷

aim (v) 🔊 /eɪm/

athletics (n) /æˈθletɪks/ sports such as running, jumping, throwing, etc.: *Kevin prefers athletics to team sports.*

atmosphere (n) 🔊 /ˈætməsfɪə(r)/

captain (n) 🔊 /ˈkæptɪn/ the person who is the leader of a group or team: *Who is the captain of your basketball team?*

certain (adj) 🔊 /ˈsɜːtn/

champion (n) /ˈtʃæmpiən/ a person, team, etc. that has won a competition: *The champion received $100,000 in prize money.*

championship (n) /ˈtʃæmpiənʃɪp/

coach (n) 🔊 /kəʊtʃ/ a person who develops a player's sports skills: *The coach helped Helen improve her running technique.*

compete (v) 🔊 /kəmˈpiːt/

competitor (n) /kəmˈpetɪtə(r)/

course (n) 🔊 /kɔːs/ an area where golf is played or where certain types of race occur: *One of the most famous race courses in the UK is Ascot.*

court (n) 🔊 /kɔːt/ an area where certain ball games are played: *There are some tennis courts near our house.*

crowd (n) 🔊 /kraʊd/

fan (n) 🔊 /fæn/

finalist (n) /ˈfaɪnəlɪst/ a finalist plays in the final of a competition: *The two finalists in the tennis match are getting ready to play.*

have a chat (verb phrase) 🔊 /ˌhæv ə ˈtʃæt/

have a go (verb phrase) 🔊 /ˌhæv ə ˈɡəʊ/

have a rest (verb phrase) 🔊 /ˌhæv ə ˈrest/

have an argument (verb phrase) 🔊 /ˌhæv ən ˈɑːɡjumənt/

have fun (verb phrase) 🔊 /ˌhæv ˈfʌn/

journalist (n) 🔊 /ˈdʒɜːnəlɪst/

loser (n) /ˈluːzə(r)/ in a final, the loser comes second: *I want to be a winner, not a loser.*

manager (n) 🔊 /ˈmænɪdʒə(r)/ the football manager chooses the team for a match: *Alex Ferguson was manager of Manchester United for 27 years.*

massive (n) 🔊 /ˈmæsɪv/

match (n) 🔊 /mætʃ/ an organised game or sport event: *Arsenal won the football match against Chelsea.*

motor racing (n) 🔊 /ˈməʊtə ˌreɪsɪŋ/ the sport of racing motor vehicles, especially cars: *Most motor racing takes part on a special track, but some also happen on closed roads.*

race (n) 🔊 /reɪs/ a competition between people, animals, cars, etc. to see which is the fastest: *Jameela came second in the 400-metre race.*

referee (n) /refəˈriː/ The official person in sports such as football who controls the match and prevents players from breaking the rules: *The referee sent off two players in the football match.*

reporter (n) 🔊 /rɪˈpɔːtə(r)/ a reporter describes the events in a match: *The reporter wrote an article for the newspaper about our golf tournament.*

rugby (n) /ˈrʌɡbi/ a form of football that is played between two teams of 13 or 15 players with an oval ball that can be carried, kicked or thrown: *Do you play rugby or football at your school?*

season (n) 🔊 /ˈsiːzn/ the period of the year when a sport is usually done: *The football season in the UK runs from August of one year until May of the next year.*

situation (n) 🔊 /ˌsɪtʃuˈeɪʃn/

skiing (n) /ˈskiːɪŋ/ the sport where you move over snow on a pair of long, narrow, flat, pieces of wood or plastic that are fastened to boots: *My parents went skiing in Italy last year.*

skilful (adj) 🔊 /ˈskɪlfl/

sponsor (n) /ˈspɒnsə(r)/ a sponsor has its name on a sportsperson's clothes: *Many companies are sponsors of British football teams.*

stadium (n) /ˈsteɪdiəm/ a large structure, usually with no roof, where people can sit and watch sport: *Azadi Stadium in Tehran holds 90,000 people.*

star (n) 🔊 /stɑː(r)/ a famous person in sport: *Usain Bolt is an athletics star.*

/i/ happy	/æ/ flag	/ɜː/ her	/ʊ/ look	/ʌ/ mum	/ɔɪ/ noisy	/ɪə/ here
/ɪ/ it	/ɑː/ art	/ɒ/ not	/uː/ you	/eɪ/ day	/aʊ/ how	/eə/ wear
/iː/ he	/e/ egg	/ɔː/ four	/ə/ sugar	/aɪ/ why	/əʊ/ go	/ʊə/ tourist

support (v) O─ /sə'pɔːt/

supporter (n) O─ /sə'pɔːtə(r)/ a person who supports a sports team: *The football supporters were all wearing scarves in their team's colour.*

team (n) O─ /tiːm/ a group of people who play a sport or game together against another group: *Are you in the hockey team?*

tournament (n) /'tʊənəmənt/ a competition in which many players or teams play games against each other: *The tournament lasted three weeks and the Spanish team won in the end.*

trophy (n) /'trəʊfi/ a large silver cup, etc. that you get for winning a competition or race: *The winner of the trophy has to return it after a year for the next winner.*

UNIT 10

break (v) O─ /breɪk/ to separate something into two or more pieces: *Faisal broke his leg in a skiing accident.*

break (n) O─ /breɪk/ a place where something has been broken: *Asma has a bad break in her arm after falling off her bike.*

bruise (v) /bruːz/ to cause a blue, brown or purple mark on the skin after a fall or a hit: *Adam has the sort of skin that bruises easily.*

bruise (n) /bruːz/ a blue, brown or purple mark on the skin after someone has fallen, been hit, etc.: *Basma fell over and has an enormous bruise on her arm.*

burn (v) O─ /bɜːn/ to injure someone with fire or heat: *If you get too close to the fire, you'll burn yourself.*

burn (n) O─ /bɜːn/ damage or an injury caused by fire or heat: *There's a cigarette burn on the carpet.*

cancel (v) O─ /'kænsl/

check-up (n) O─ /'tʃek ˌʌp/

cope (v) O─ /kəʊp/

cut (v) O─ /kʌt/ to make an opening, wound or mark in something with a sharp tool: *Be careful you don't cut yourself with that sharp knife.*

cut (n) O─ /kʌt/ an injury or opening in the skin made with a knife: *Saad has a deep cut on his leg.*

disgusting (adj) O─ /dɪs'gʌstɪŋ/

dizzy (adj) /'dɪzi/

embarrassed (about) (adj) O─ /ɪm'bærəst (əˌbaʊt)/ feeling uncomfortable or shy about something silly you have done: *I felt so embarrassed when I walked into the door.*

enthusiastic (about) (adj) O─ /ɪnθjuːzi'æstɪk (əˌbaʊt)/ full of excitement and interest in something: *Jane is very enthusiastic about the new project.*

faint (v) O─ /feɪnt/

filling (n) O─ /'fɪlɪŋ/

filthy (adj) /'fɪlθi/

fond (of) (adj) /'fɒnd (əv)/ liking a person or thing: *My aunt is very fond of cats.*

injure (v) O─ /'ɪndʒə(r)/ to harm or hurt yourself, or someone else, physically, especially in an accident: *The goalkeeper seriously injured himself when he hit the goalpost.*

injury (n) O─ /'ɪndʒəri/ harm done to someone's body, especially in an accident: *They escaped from the accident with only minor injuries.*

interested (in) (adj) O─ /'ɪntrəstɪd (ɪn)/ wanting to hear or know more about something: *They weren't interested in my news at all!*

keen (on) (adj) O─ /'kiːn (ɒn)/ very interested in something: *She failed the first time but she's keen to have another go.*

not at all (modifier) O─ /ˌnɒt ət 'ɔːl/

patient (n) O─ /'peɪʃnt/

quite (modifier) O─ /kwaɪt/

really (modifier) O─ /'riːəli/

ridiculous (adj) O─ /rɪ'dɪkjələs/

scratch (v) O─ /skrætʃ/ to make a mark on the skin with something sharp: *The cat will scratch you if you annoy him.*

scratch (n) O─ /skrætʃ/ a cut or mark that was made by something sharp rubbing your skin: *How did you get that scratch on your face?*

specialist (n) O─ /'speʃəlɪst/

sprain (v) /spreɪn/ to injure part of your body, especially your wrist or ankle, by suddenly bending or turning it: *Emir sprained his ankle playing basketball last night.*

sprain (n) /spreɪn/ an injury to part of your body, especially your wrist or ankle, from suddenly bending or turning it: *Maya has a bad sprain in her wrist. It's very bruised and swollen.*

stressed out (about) (adj) O─ /ˌstrest 'aʊt (əˌbaʊt)/ too anxious and tired to be able to relax: *He was feeling very stressed out about his job.*

terrified (of) (adj) /'terɪfaɪd (əv)/ very afraid: *I'm absolutely terrified of snakes.*

very (modifier) O─ /'veri/

weird (adj) O─ /wɪəd/

worried (about) (adj) O─ /'wʌrid (əˌbaʊt)/ thinking that something bad has happened or will happen: *Jenna is really worried about her exams.*

/p/ **pen**	/d/ **dog**	/tʃ/ **beach**	/v/ **very**	/s/ **speak**	/ʒ/ **television**	/n/ **now**	/r/ **radio**
/b/ **big**	/k/ **can**	/dʒ/ **job**	/θ/ **think**	/z/ **zoo**	/h/ **house**	/ŋ/ **sing**	/j/ **yes**
/t/ **two**	/g/ **good**	/f/ **food**	/ð/ **then**	/ʃ/ **she**	/m/ **meat**	/l/ **late**	/w/ **we**

Vocabulary notebook

Vocabulary notebook is a list of useful vocabulary from each unit. Use your dictionar to check meanings and write notes about these words in the spaces given.

STARTER UNIT

apartment (n) /əˈpɑːtmənt/

bad (adj) /bæd/

balcony (n) ⚲ /ˈbælkəni/

bathroom (n) /ˈbɑːθruːm/

bedroom (n) /ˈbedruːm/

boring (adj) /ˈbɔːrɪŋ/

borrow (v) /ˈbɒrəʊ/

brilliant (at) (adj) /ˈbrɪliənt (ət)/

building (n) /ˈbɪldɪŋ/

clever (adj) /ˈklevə(r)/

corner (n) /ˈkɔːnə(r)/

different (adj) /ˈdɪfrənt/

difficult (adj) /ˈdɪfɪkəlt/

dining room (n) /ˈdaɪnɪŋ ˌruːm/

easy (adj) /ˈiːzi/

exactly (adv) /ɪgˈzæktli/

famous (adj) /ˈfeɪməs/

favourite (adj) /ˈfeɪvərɪt/

flag (n) /flæg/

floor (n) /flɔː(r)/

friendly (adj) /ˈfrendli/

fun (adj) /fʌn/

garden (n) /ˈgɑːdn/

good (at) (adj) /ˈgʊd (ət)/

head teacher (n) /ˌhed ˈtiːtʃə(r)/

interesting (adj) /ˈɪntrəstɪŋ/

jacket (n) /ˈdʒækɪt/

kitchen (n) /ˈkɪtʃɪn/

laptop (n) ⚲ /ˈlæptɒp/

living room (n) /ˈlɪvɪŋ ˌruːm/

modern (adj) /ˈmɒdn/

nice (adj) /naɪs/

noisy (adj) /ˈnɔɪzi/

notes (n) /nəʊts/

old (adj) /əʊld/

plasma TV (n) ⚲ /ˌplæzmə ˌtiː ˈviː/

quiet (adj) /ˈkwaɪət/

revise (v) /rɪˈvaɪz/

rubbish (at) (adj) /ˈrʌbɪʃ (ət)/

science (n) /ˈsaɪəns/

security camera (n) /sɪˈkjʊərəti ˌkæmərə/

sliding door (n) /ˌslaɪdɪŋ ˈdɔː(r)/

strange (adj) /streɪndʒ/

swimming pool (n) /ˈswɪmɪŋ ˌpuːl/

terrace (n) ⚲ /ˈterəs/

unfriendly (adj) /ʌnˈfrendli/

window (n) /ˈwɪndəʊ/

UNIT 1

about (adv) /əˈbaʊt/

afternoon (n) /ˌɑːftəˈnuːn/

always (adv) /ˈɔːlweɪz/

appearance (n) /əˈpɪərəns/

belief (n) /bɪˈliːf/

character (n) /ˈkærəktə(r)/

delicious (adj) ⚲ /dɪˈlɪʃəs/

doesn't matter (noun phrase) ⚲
/ˌdʌznt ˈmætə(r)/

evening (n) /ˈiːvnɪŋ/

factfile (n) ⚲ /ˈfæktfaɪl/

hammock (n) ⚲ /ˈhæmək/

in particular (noun phrase)
/ˌɪn pəˈtɪkjələ(r)/

including (prep) /ɪnˈkluːdɪŋ/

language (n) /ˈlæŋgwɪdʒ/

lesson (n) /ˈlesn/

main (adj) /meɪn/

mall (n) /mɔːl/

medium-sized (adj) ⚲ /ˈmiːdiəm ˌsaɪzd/

mixed race (adj) /ˌmɪkst ˈreɪs/

morning (n) /ˈmɔːnɪŋ/

multicultural (adj) /ˌmʌltiˈkʌltʃərəl/

nation (n) /ˈneɪʃn/

nearly (adv) /ˈnɪəli/

neighbour (n) /ˈneɪbə(r)/

never (adv) /ˈnevə(r)/

often (adv) /ˈɒfn, ˈɒftən/

outside (adj) /ˈaʊtsaɪd/

particular (adj) /pəˈtɪkjələ(r)/

per cent (n) /pə ˈsent/

perfect (adj) /ˈpɜːfɪkt/

popular (adj) /ˈpɒpjələ(r)/

pronunciation (n) /prənʌnsiˈeɪʃn/

religion (n) /rɪˈlɪdʒən/

routine (n) /ruːˈtiːn/

scenery (n) ⚲ /ˈsiːnəri/

sometimes (adv) /ˈsʌmtaɪmz/

tap (n) /tæp/

tired (adj) /ˈtaɪəd/

university (n) /juːnɪˈvɜːsəti/

usually (adv) /ˈjuːʒuəli/

website (n) /ˈwebsaɪt/

weekend (n) /wiːkˈend/

world (n) /wɜːld/

UNIT 2

abroad (adj) /əˈbrɔːd/

advantage (n) /ədˈvɑːntɪdʒ/

afterwards (adv) /ˈɑːftəwədz/

agree (v) /əˈgriː/

alive (adj) /əˈlaɪv/

amazing (adj) /əˈmeɪzɪŋ/

around (prep) /əˈraʊnd/

banknote (n) ⚲ /ˈbæŋknəʊt/

/i/ happy	/æ/ flag	/ɜː/ her	/ʊ/ look	/ʌ/ mum	/ɔɪ/ noisy	/ɪə/ here
/ɪ/ it	/ɑː/ art	/ɒ/ not	/uː/ you	/eɪ/ day	/aʊ/ how	/eə/ wear
/iː/ he	/e/ egg	/ɔː/ four	/ə/ sugar	/aɪ/ why	/əʊ/ go	/ʊə/ tourist

be into (verb phrase) /ˌbiː ˈɪntuː/

be mad about (verb phrase)
/ˌbi ˈmæd əˌbaʊt/

because (conjunction) /bɪˈkɒz, bɪˈkəz/

bird (n) /bɜːd/

boat (n) /bəʊt/

break (n) /breɪk/

can't stand (v) /ˌkɑːnt ˈstænd/

capital (adj) / (n) /ˈkæpɪtl/

catch (v) /kætʃ/

colourful (adj) ⚷ /ˈkʌləfl/

common (adj) /ˈkɒmən/

compare (v) /kəmˈpeə(r)/

competition (n) /kɒmpəˈtɪʃn/

computer game (n) /kəmˈpjuːtə ˌgeɪm/

cook (v) /kʊk/

cool (adj) /kuːl/

cousin (n) /ˈkʌzn/

detail (n) /ˈdiːteɪl/

disadvantage (n) /dɪsədˈvɑːntɪdʒ/

dislike (v) / (n) /dɪsˈlaɪk/

early (adj) /ˈɜːli/

enter (v) /ˈentə(r)/

event (n) /ɪˈvent/

except (prep) /ɪkˈsept/

exciting (adj) /ɪkˈsaɪtɪŋ/

fan (n) /fæn/

focus (v) /ˈfəʊkəs/

foreign (adj) /ˈfɒrən/

free time (n) /ˌfriː ˈtaɪm/

gym (n) ⚷ /dʒɪm/

happen (v) /ˈhæpən/

have (something) in common
(verb phrase) /ˌhæv ˌ(...) ɪn ˈkɒmən/

have to (v) /ˈhæf ˌtuː, tə/

helpful (adj) /ˈhelpfl/

hobby (n) /ˈhɒbi//

household good (n) /ˌhaʊshəʊld ˈɡʊd/

idea (n) /aɪˈdɪə/

important (adj) /ɪmˈpɔːtnt/

instructions (n) /ɪnˈstrʌkʃnz/

keen (adj) /kiːn/

keep fit (verb phrase) /ˌkiːp ˈfɪt/

key (n) /kiː/

kind (adj) /kaɪnd/

look after (v) /ˈlʊk ˌɑːftə(r)/

lost (adj) /lɒst/

map (n) /mæp/

mind (v) /maɪnd/

most (determiner) /məʊst/

nearby (adj) /ˈnɪəbaɪ/

online (n) /ɒnˈlaɪn/

package (n) /ˈpækɪdʒ/

post (a message) (v) /ˌpəʊst (ə ˈmesɪdʒ)/

problem (n) /ˈprɒbləm/

profile (n) /ˈprəʊfaɪl/

questionnaire (n) ⚷ /kwestʃəˈneə(r)/

reckon (v) /ˈrekən/

regularly (adv) /ˈregjələli/

roast dinner (n) ⚷ /ˌrəʊst ˈdɪnə(r)/

score (n) /skɔː(r)/

set (the table) (v) /ˌset (ðə ˈteɪbl)/

share (v) /ʃeə(r)/

something (pronoun) /ˈsʌmθɪŋ/

spend (v) /spend/

suppose (v) /səˈpəʊz/

together (adv) /təˈgeðə(r)/

traditional (adj) /trəˈdɪʃənl/

trainers (n) ⚷ /ˈtreɪnəz/

trendy (adj) ⚷ /ˈtrendi/

twice (adv) /twaɪs/

type (n) /taɪp/

unusual (adj) /ʌnˈjuːʒuəl/

useful (adj) /ˈjuːsfl/

vacuum cleaner (n) ⚷
/ˈvækjuəm ˌkliːnə(r)/

way of life (noun phrase) /ˌweɪ əv ˈlaɪf/

whatever (determiner) wɒtˈevə(r)/

worry (v) /ˈwʌri/

UNIT 3 ▪▪▪

ability (n) /əˈbɪləti/

absolutely (adv) /ˈæbsəluːtli/

adventure (n) /ədˈventʃə(r)/

annual (adj) /ˈænjuəl/

barbecue (n) ⚷ /ˈbɑːbɪkjuː/

beach (n) /biːtʃ/

boat trip (n) /ˈbəʊt ˌtrɪp/

build (v) /bɪld/

camel (n) ⚷ /ˈkæml/

camping (n) /ˈkæmpɪŋ/

climb (v) /klaɪm/

clock (n) /klɒk/

coast (n) /kəʊst/

cold (adj) /kəʊld/

completely (adv) /kəmˈpliːtli/

connect (v) /kəˈnekt/

conservation (n) ⚷ /kɒnsəˈveɪʃn/

continent (n) /ˈkɒntɪnənt/

coral reef (n) ⚷ /ˈkɒrəl ˌriːf/

crazy (adj) /ˈkreɪzi/

dense (adj) ⚷ /dens/

destination (n) ⚷ /destɪˈneɪʃn/

do an exam (verb phrase) /ˌduː ən ɪgˈzæm/

do exercise (verb phrase) /ˌduː ˈeksəsaɪz/

do the cleaning (verb phrase)
/ˌduː ðə ˈkliːnɪŋ/

/p/ pen	/d/ dog	/tʃ/ beach	/v/ very	/s/ speak	/ʒ/ television	/n/ now	/r/ radio
/b/ big	/k/ can	/dʒ/ job	/θ/ think	/z/ zoo	/h/ house	/ŋ/ sing	/j/ yes
/t/ two	/g/ good	/f/ food	/ð/ then	/ʃ/ she	/m/ meat	/l/ late	/w/ we

Vocabulary notebook

dolphin (n) o⃥ /ˈdɒlfɪn/ ....

enjoy (v) /ɪnˈdʒɔɪ/ ....

everyone (pronoun) /ˈevriwʌn/ ....

expect (v) /ɪkˈspekt/ ....

experience (n) /ɪkˈspɪəriəns/ ....

expert (n) /ˈekspɜːt/ ....

explorer (n) o⃥ /ɪkˈsplɔːrə(r)/ ....

fire (n) /ˈfaɪə(r)/ ....

fishing (n) /ˈfɪʃɪŋ/ ....

float (v) /fləʊt/ ....

guide (n) /gaɪd/ ....

hill walking (n) /ˈhɪl ˌwɔːkɪŋ/ ....

horse riding (n) /ˈhɔːs ˌraɪdɪŋ/ ....

island (n) /ˈaɪlənd/ ....

jungle (n) o⃥ /ˈdʒʌŋgl/ ....

key ring (n) /ˈkiː ˌrɪŋ/ ....

leaflet (n) o⃥ /ˈliːflət/ ....

local (adj) /ˈləʊkl/ ....

make a decision (verb phrase) /ˌmeɪk ə dɪˈsɪʒn/ ....

make a mess (verb phrase) /ˌmeɪk ə ˈmes/ ....

make a phone call (verb phrase) /ˌmeɪk ə ˈfəʊn ˌkɔːl/ ....

money-raising (adj) o⃥ /ˈmʌni ˌreɪzɪŋ/ ....

natural world (n) /ˌnætʃrəl ˈwɜːld/ ....

nowadays (adv) o⃥ /ˈnaʊədeɪz/ ....

organise (v) /ˈɔːgənaɪz/ ....

overland (adj) o⃥ /ˈəʊvəlænd/ ....

pay (v) /peɪ/ ....

peaceful (adj) /ˈpiːsfl/ ....

plan (v) /plæn/ ....

postcard (n) o⃥ /ˈpəʊstkɑːd/ ....

problem solving (n) /ˈprɒbləm ˌsɒlvɪŋ/ ....

project (n) /ˈprɒdʒekt/ ....

protect (v) /prəˈtekt/ ....

puzzle (n) o⃥ /ˈpʌzl/ ....

quiz (n) o⃥ /kwɪz/ ....

rain (v) /reɪn/ ....

recommend (v) /rekəˈmend/ ....

relaxation (n) o⃥ /riːlækˈseɪʃn/ ....

relaxing (adj) /rɪˈlæksɪŋ/ ....

research (n) /rɪˈsɜːtʃ, ˈriːsɜːtʃ/ ....

rest (n) /rest/ ....

sailing (n) /ˈseɪlɪŋ/ ....

sand dune (n) o⃥ /ˈsænd ˌdjuːn/ ....

section (n) /ˈsekʃn/ ....

shelter (n) /ˈʃeltə(r)/ ....

shine (v) /ʃaɪn/ ....

sightseeing (n) o⃥ /ˈsaɪtsiːɪŋ/ ....

skills (n) /skɪlz/ ....

souvenir (n) o⃥ /suːvəˈnɪə(r)/ ....

survival skill (n) o⃥ /səˈvaɪvl ˌskɪl/ ....

take part (v) /ˌteɪk ˈpɑːt/ ....

teamwork (n) o⃥ /ˈtiːmwɜːk/ ....

teenager (n) o⃥ /ˈtiːneɪdʒə(r)/ ....

truly (adv) /ˈtruːli/ ....

typical (adj) /ˈtɪpɪkl/ ....

ultimate (adj) /ˈʌltɪmət/ ....

weather (n) /ˈweðə(r)/ ....

wet (adj) /wet/ ....

windsurfing (n) o⃥ /ˈwɪndsɜːfɪŋ/ ....

young (adj) /jʌŋ/ ....

UNIT 4 ■ ■ ■

amount (n) /əˈmaʊnt/ ....

ancient (adj) /ˈeɪnʃənt/ ....

approximately (adv) /əˈprɒksɪmətli/ ....

available (adj) /əˈveɪləbl/ ....

balanced (adj) /ˈbælənst/ ....

cause (n) /kɔːz/ ....

cheap (adj) /tʃiːp/ ....

comment (v) /ˈkɒmənt/ ....

concentrate (v) /ˈkɒnsntreɪt/ ....

conclusion (n) /kənˈkluːʒn/ ....

convenient (adj) /kənˈviːniənt/ ....

couple (n) /ˈkʌpl/ ....

decide (v) /dɪˈsaɪd/ ....

demonstrate (adj) /ˈdemənstreɪt/ ....

diet (n) /ˈdaɪət/ ....

fast food (n) /ˌfɑːst ˈfuːd/ ....

feel ill (verb phrase) /ˌfiːl ˈɪl/ ....

fizzy drink (n) o⃥ /ˌfɪzi ˈdrɪŋk/ ....

following (adj) /ˈfɒləʊɪŋ/ ....

fructose (n) o⃥ /ˈfrʌktəʊs/ ....

get fat (verb phrase) /ˌget ˈfæt/ ....

health (n) /helθ/ ....

healthy (adj) /ˈhelθi/ ....

heritage site (n) o⃥ /ˈherɪtɪdʒ ˌsaɪt/ ....

high (adj) /haɪ/ ....

honey (n) o⃥ /ˈhʌni/ ....

introduction (n) /ɪntrəˈdʌkʃn/ ....

location (n) /ləʊˈkeɪʃn/ ....

mad about (verb phrase) /ˈmæd əˌbaʊt/ ....

menu (n) /ˈmenjuː/ ....

opinion (n) /əˈpɪnjən/ ....

option (n) /ˈɒpʃn/ ....

per (prep) /pɜː(r), pə/ ....

quick (adj) /kwɪk/ ....

relative (n) /ˈrelətɪv/ ....

repetition (n) o⃥ /repəˈtɪʃn/ ....

result (n) /rɪˈzʌlt/ ....

serve (v) /sɜːv/ ....

snack (n) o⃥ /snæk/ ....

solution (n) /səˈluːʃn/ ....

source (n) /sɔːs/ ....

special (adj) /ˈspeʃl/ ....

/i/ happy	/æ/ flag	/ɜː/ her	/ʊ/ look	/ʌ/ mum	/ɔɪ/ noisy	/ɪə/ here
/ɪ/ it	/ɑː/ art	/ɒ/ not	/uː/ you	/eɪ/ day	/aʊ/ how	/eə/ wear
/iː/ he	/e/ egg	/ɔː/ four	/ə/ sugar	/aɪ/ why	/əʊ/ go	/ʊə/ tourist

spray (n) /spreɪ/
sweet (adj) /swiːt/
sweeten (v) ⚷ /ˈswiːtn/
taste (v) /teɪst/
topic (n) /ˈtɒpɪk/
unhealthy (adj) ⚷ /ʌnˈhelθi/
vegetarian (n) ⚷ /ˌvedʒəˈteəriən/
verdict (n) ⚷ /ˈvɜːdɪkt/
weight (n) /weɪt/
well (adj) /wel/
worried (adj) /ˈwʌrid/

UNIT 5

afford (v) /əˈfɔːd/
brain (n) /breɪn/
cap (n) /kæp/
card (n) /kɑːd/
century (n) /ˈsentʃəri/
circuit (n) /ˈsɜːkɪt/
clearly (adv) /ˈklɪəli/
comedy (n) /ˈkɒmədi/
correct (adj) /kəˈrekt/
cry (v) /kraɪ/
excellent (adj) /ˈeksələnt/
fact (n) /fækt/
funny (adj) /ˈfʌni/
half (n) /hɑːf/
helicopter (n) ⚷ /ˈhelɪkɒptə(r)/
imagination (n) /ɪˌmædʒɪˈneɪʃn/
international (adj) /ˌɪntəˈnæʃnəl/
joke (n) /dʒəʊk/
landmark (n) ⚷ /ˈlændmɑːk/
line (n) /laɪn/
lose (v) /luːz/
match (n) /mætʃ/
medical (adj) /ˈmedɪkl/
meeting (n) /ˈmiːtɪŋ/
memory (n) /ˈmeməri/
nickname (n) /ˈnɪkneɪm/
noise (n) /nɔɪz/
organised (adj) /ˈɔːɡənaɪzd/
pie (n) ⚷ /paɪ/
recipe (n) ⚷ /ˈresəpi/
remember (v) /rɪˈmembə(r)/
seat (n) /siːt/
symbol (n) /ˈsɪmbl/
terrible (adj) /ˈterəbl/
ticket (n) /ˈtɪkɪt/
timeline (n) ⚷ /ˈtaɪmlaɪn/
tragedy (n) ⚷ /ˈtrædʒədi/
train (v) /treɪn/
win (v) /wɪn/
world record (n) /ˌwɜːld ˈrekɔːd/
wrong (adj) /rɒŋ/

UNIT 6

accident (n) /ˈæksɪdənt/
after (conjunction) /ˈɑːftə(r)/
alive (adj) /əˈlaɪv/
allow (v) /əˈlaʊ/
as soon as (conjunction) /əz ˈsuːn əz/
attract (v) /əˈtrækt/
back (n) /bæk/
base jumping (n) ⚷ /ˈbeɪs ˌdʒʌmpɪŋ/
cave (n) ⚷ /keɪv/
coal (n) /kəʊl/
competitor (n) ⚷ /kəmˈpetɪtə(r)/
costume (n) ⚷ /ˈkɒstjuːm/
crash (v) /kræʃ/
crowd (n) /kraʊd/
dangerous (adj) /ˈdeɪndʒərəs/
die (v) /daɪ/
diving suit (n) ⚷ /ˈdaɪvɪŋ ˌsuːt/
equivalent (adj) /ɪˈkwɪvələnt/
extreme (adj) /ɪkˈstriːm/
firewalker (n) ⚷ /ˈfaɪəwɔːkə(r)/
fix (v) /fɪks/
foot (n) /fʊt/
freediver (n) ⚷ /ˈfriːdaɪvə(r)/
frozen (adj) /ˈfrəʊzn/
fundraising (n) ⚷ /ˈfʌndreɪzɪŋ/
helmet (n) ⚷ /ˈhelmɪt/
incredible (adj) ⚷ /ɪnˈkredəbl/
inspire (v) ⚷ /ɪnˈspaɪə(r)/
journalist (n) /ˈdʒɜːnəlɪst/
king (n) /kɪŋ/
lady (n) /ˈleɪdi/
lorry (n) /ˈlɒri/
metal (n) /ˈmetl/
nervous (adj) /ˈnɜːvəs/
old-fashioned (adj) /ˌəʊld ˈfæʃnd/
omelette (n) ⚷ /ˈɒmlət/
oxygen (n) ⚷ /ˈɒksɪdʒən/
personality (n) /ˌpɜːsəˈnæləti/
quality (n) /ˈkwɒləti/
raise (v) /reɪz/
ramp (n) ⚷ /ræmp/
relaxed (adj) /rɪˈlækst/
rescue (n) /ˈreskjuː/
risk (n) /rɪsk/
rope (n) /rəʊp/
rule (n) /ruːl/
scared (adj) /skeəd/
scary (adj) /ˈskeəri/
shark (n) ⚷ /ʃɑːk/
stunt (n) ⚷ /stʌnt/
suddenly (adv) /ˈsʌdənli/
sum (n) /sʌm/

/p/ pen	/d/ dog	/tʃ/ beach	/v/ very	/s/ speak	/ʒ/ television	/n/ now	/r/ radio
/b/ big	/k/ can	/dʒ/ job	/θ/ think	/z/ zoo	/h/ house	/ŋ/ sing	/j/ yes
/t/ two	/g/ good	/f/ food	/ð/ then	/ʃ/ she	/m/ meat	/l/ late	/w/ we

Vocabulary notebook

surfer (n) 0̶ /'sɜːfə(r)/
survive (v) /sə'vaɪv/
tank (n) /tæŋk/
temperature (n) /'temprətʃə(r)/
terrified (adj) 0̶ /'terɪfaɪd/
tourist attraction (n) /'tʊərɪst ə,trækʃn/
twin (n) /twɪn/
wall (n) /wɔːl/
wave (n) /weɪv/
west (adj) /west/
when (conjunction) /wen/
while (conjunction) /waɪl/
windy (adj) 0̶ /'wɪndi/
without (prep) /wɪ'ðaʊt/

respected (adj) /rɪ'spektɪd/
sad (adj) /sæd/
skill (n) /skɪl/
skilled (adj) /skɪld/
solve (v) /sɒlv/
style (n) /staɪl/
successfully (adv) /sək'sesfəli/
summary (n) /'sʌməri/
talent (n) /'tælənt/
translation (n) /træns'leɪʃn/
unfortunate (adj) /ʌn'fɔːtʃənət/
vase (n) 0̶ /vɑːz/
version (n) /'vɜːʃn/
well-paid (adj) 0̶ /,wel 'peɪd/

UNIT 7 ▮▮▮▮

admire (v) /əd'maɪə(r)/
calculator (n) 0̶ /'kælkjuleɪtə(r)/
career (n) /kə'rɪə(r)/
clear (adj) /klɪə(r)/
compete (v) /kəm'piːt/
definitely (adv) /'defɪnətli/
diplomat (n) 0̶ /'dɪpləmæt/
disabled (adj) /dɪs'eɪbld/
equation (n) 0̶ /ɪ'kweɪʒn/
equipment (n) /ɪ'kwɪpmənt/
eventually (adv) /ɪ'ventʃuəli/
far (adj) /fɑː(r)/
fast (adj) /fɑːst/
fluent (adj) 0̶ /'fluːənt/
fortunate (adj) 0̶ /'fɔːtʃənət/
hard (adj) /hɑːd/
illegal (adj) /ɪ'liːgl/
illness (n) /'ɪlnəs/
incredibly (adv) 0̶ /ɪn'kredəbli/
label (n) /'leɪbl/
law (n) /lɔː/
life (n) /laɪf/
minimum (n) /'mɪnɪməm/
novel (n) /'nɒvl/
own (v) /əʊn/
play (n) /pleɪ/
poem (n) /'pəʊɪm/
poet (n) 0̶ /'pəʊɪt/
poster (n) 0̶ /'pəʊstə(r)/
price (n) /praɪs/
prodigy (n) 0̶ /'prɒdədʒi/
product (n) /'prɒdʌkt/
psychologist (n) 0̶ /saɪ'kɒlədʒɪst/
publisher (n) 0̶ /'pʌblɪʃə(r)/
quiz master (n) 0̶ /'kwɪz ,mɑːstə(r)/
realistic (adj) /riːə'lɪstɪk/
respect (v) /rɪ'spekt/

UNIT 8 ▮▮▮▮

air (n) /eə(r)/
article (n) /'ɑːtɪkl/
beginning (n) /bɪ'gɪnɪŋ/
cable car (n) /'keɪbl ,kɑː(r)/
countryside (n) /'kʌntrisaɪd/
during (prep) /'djʊərɪŋ/
edge (n) /edʒ/
electric (adj) /ɪ'lektrɪk/
essential (adj) /ɪ'senʃl/
everywhere (adv) /'evriweə(r)/
exhausting (adj) 0̶ /ɪg'zɔːstɪŋ/
government (n) /'gʌvənmənt/
guest (n) /gest/
heart (n) /hɑːt/
hold on (v) /,həʊld 'ɒn/
hope (v) /həʊp/
imagine (v) /ɪ'mædʒɪn/
increase (v) /ɪn'kriːs/
indoors (adv) /ɪn'dɔːz/
megacity (n) 0̶ /'megəsɪti/
observation deck (n) 0̶
/ɒbzə'veɪʃn ,dek/
obviously (adv) /'ɒbviəsli/
pavilion (n) 0̶ /pə'vɪliən/
percentage (n) /pə'sentɪdʒ/
planet (n) /'plænɪt/
positive (adj) /'pɒzətɪv/
predict (v) /prɪ'dɪkt/
public transport (n) /,pʌblɪk 'trænspɔːt/
railway line (n) /'reɪlweɪ ,laɪn/
run out of (v) /,rʌn 'aʊt əv/
sign (n) /saɪn/
solar energy (n) 0̶ /'səʊlər ,enədʒi/
solve (v) /sɒlv/
speed (n) /spiːd/
tightly (adv) /'taɪtli/
ultra-modern (adj) 0̶ /'ʌltrə ,mɒdn/

/i/ happy	/æ/ flag	/ɜː/ her	/ʊ/ look	/ʌ/ mum	/ɔɪ/ noisy	/ɪə/ here
/ɪ/ it	/ɑː/ art	/ɒ/ not	/uː/ you	/eɪ/ day	/aʊ/ how	/eə/ wear
/iː/ he	/e/ egg	/ɔː/ four	/ə/ sugar	/aɪ/ why	/əʊ/ go	/ʊə/ tourist

whole (n) /həʊl/
winter (n) /'wɪntə(r)/

UNIT 9

angrily (adv) /'æŋgrəli/
arrangement (n) /ə'reɪndʒmənt/
club (n) /klʌb/
consecutive (adj) ⚷ /kən'sekjətɪv/
contact (v) /'kɒntækt/
F1 driver (n) /ˌfɔːmjələ 'wʌn ˌdraɪvə(r)/
intention (n) /ɪn'tenʃn/
invitation (n) /ˌɪnvɪ'teɪʃn/
kart (n) ⚷ /kɑːt/
publicity (n) /pʌb'lɪsəti/
racing (n) /'reɪsɪŋ/
rally car (n) ⚷ /'ræli ˌkɑː(r)/
red card (n) /ˌred 'kɑːd/
sportsperson (n) ⚷ /'spɔːtspɜːsn/
suggest (v) /sə'dʒest/
track (n) /træk/

UNIT 10

agoraphobia (n) ⚷ /ˌægərə'fəʊbiə/
amusement park (n) ⚷ /ə'mjuːzmənt ˌpɑːk/
ankle (n) /'æŋkl/
apparently (adv) /ə'pærəntli/
appointment (n) /ə'pɔɪntmənt/
back (n) /bæk/
bone (n) /bəʊn/
careful (adj) /'keəfl/
coach (n) /kəʊtʃ/
danger (n) /'deɪndʒə(r)/
deep-sea fisherman (n) ⚷ /ˌdiːp ˌsiː 'fɪʃəmən/
dentist (n) /'dentɪst/
dirt (n) /dɜːt/
dirty (adj) /'dɜːti/
elbow (n) /'elbəʊ/
emergency services (n) /iˌmɜːdʒənsi 'sɜːvɪsɪz/
erupt (v) /ɪ'rʌpt/
exotic (adj) /ɪg'zɒtɪk/
factory (n) /'fæktri/
fair play (n) /ˌfeə 'pleɪ/
fancy (v) /'fænsi/
fear (n) /fɪə(r)/
ferry (n) ⚷ /'feri/
finger (n) /'fɪŋgə(r)/
ground (n) /graʊnd/
guess (v) /ges/
handle (n) /'hændl/

hospital (n) /'hɒspɪtl/
hurt (v) /hɜːt/
in spite of (conjunction) /ɪn 'spaɪt əv/
insect (n) /'ɪnsekt/
knee (n) /niː/
machinery (n) /mə'ʃiːnəri/
owner (n) /'əʊnə(r)/
phobia (n) ⚷ /'fəʊbiə/
public (n) /'pʌblɪk/
quickly (adv) /'kwɪkli/
raincoat (n) ⚷ /'reɪnkəʊt/
refuse collector (n) ⚷ /'refjuːs kəˌlektə(r)/
roller coaster (n) ⚷ /'rəʊlə ˌkəʊstə(r)/
shoulder (n) /'ʃəʊldə(r)/
silly (adj) /'sɪli/
storm (n) /stɔːm/
suffer (v) /'sʌfə(r)/
thrill (n) ⚷ /θrɪl/
toe (n) /təʊ/
unnecessary (adj) /ʌn'nesəsəri/
unpleasant (adj) /ʌn'pleznt/
volcano (n) ⚷ /vɒl'keɪnəʊ/
volcanologist (n) ⚷ /ˌvɒlkə'nɒlədʒɪst/
water ride (n) /'wɔːtə ˌraɪd/
wild (n) /waɪld/
wonderful (adj) /'wʌndəfl/

/p/ pen	/d/ dog	/tʃ/ beach	/v/ very	/s/ speak	/ʒ/ television	/n/ now	/r/ radio
/b/ big	/k/ can	/dʒ/ job	/θ/ think	/z/ zoo	/h/ house	/ŋ/ sing	/j/ yes
/t/ two	/g/ good	/f/ food	/ð/ then	/ʃ/ she	/m/ meat	/l/ late	/w/ we

In the *Oxford Student's Dictionary*, words marked with a key symbol ⚷O are part of the Oxford 3000™ list. This is a list of the 3000 most useful and important words to learn in English.

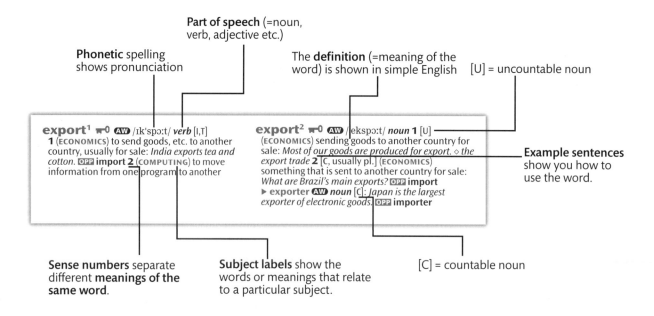

Phonetic spelling shows pronunciation

Part of speech (=noun, verb, adjective etc.)

The **definition** (=meaning of the word) is shown in simple English   [U] = uncountable noun

export¹ ⚷O **AW** /ɪkˈspɔːt/ *verb* [I,T]
1 (ECONOMICS) to send goods, etc. to another country, usually for sale: *India exports tea and cotton.* **OPP** import **2** (COMPUTING) to move information from one program to another

export² ⚷O **AW** /ˈekspɔːt/ *noun* **1** [U]
(ECONOMICS) sending goods to another country for sale: *Most of our goods are produced for export.* ◇ *the export trade* **2** [C, usually pl.] (ECONOMICS) something that is sent to another country for sale: *What are Brazil's main exports?* **OPP** import
▶ **exporter** **AW** *noun* [C]: *Japan is the largest exporter of electronic goods.* **OPP** importer

Example sentences show you how to use the word.

Sense numbers separate different **meanings of the same word**.

Subject labels show the words or meanings that relate to a particular subject.

[C] = countable noun

| **STUDY FOCUS** | **Dictionary entries** |

The dictionary contains a lot of additional information about Oxford 3000 words which will help you to expand your vocabulary. It is important to understand how this information is presented in each dictionary entry.

1 Look at the dictionary entry for *export* and read the labels.

2 The word *export* has two dictionary entries. Which two parts of speech can it be?

....

....

3 Look for the OPP (= opposite meaning) labels in the entry. What is the opposite of *exporter*?

....

....

4 How many different meanings does *export* (verb) have?

....

....

5 Read the example sentence and circle the correct subject label.

He exported the contact information from his email to the database. **COMPUTING / ECONOMICS**

6 Look at the dictionary entry for *culture*. How many meanings does it have?

....

culture ⚷O **AW** /ˈkʌltʃə(r)/ *noun* **1** [C,U]
(SOCIAL STUDIES) the customs, ideas, beliefs, etc. of a particular society, country, etc.: *the language and culture of the Aztecs* ◇ *people from many different cultures* **2** [U] (ARTS AND MEDIA) art, literature, music, etc.: *London has always been a centre of culture.* **3** [C] (BIOLOGY) a group of cells or bacteria, especially taken from a person or an animal and grown for medical or scientific study: *Yoghurt is made from active cultures.*

7 Find the three subject labels for *culture*. Read these example sentences and write the correct subject label.

1 *The Moroccan city of Essaouira is full of culture and history.*

....

2 *In the experiment, scientists looked at different cultures of cells.*

....

3 *This article is about the language and culture of the Arab people.*

....

8 Look at the dictionary entry for *race*. Find three verbs that are often used with *race* (noun). Complete the sentences using the correct form of the verb.

> **race¹** 🔊 /reɪs/ *noun* **1** [C] a ~ (against/with sb/sth); a ~ for sth/to do sth a competition between people, animals, cars, etc. to see which is the fastest or to see which can achieve sth first: *to run/win/lose a race* ◇ *to come first/second/last **in a race*** ◇ *the race for the presidency* ◇ *the race to find a cure for Aids* ◇ *Rescuing victims of the earthquake is now **a race against time**.* **2 the races** [pl.] (*BrE*) (SPORT) an occasion when a number of horse races are held in one place **3** [C,U] one of the groups into which people can be divided according to the colour of their skin, their hair type, the shape of their face, etc. ➍ look at **human race 4** [C] a group of people who have the same language, customs, history, etc. **IDM the rat race** → RAT
>
> **race²** 🔊 /reɪs/ *verb* **1** [I,T] ~ (against/with sb/sth); ~ sb/sth to have a competition with sb/sth to find out who is the fastest or to see who can do sth first: *I'll race you home.* **2** [I,T] to go very fast or to move sb/sth very fast: *We raced up the stairs.* ◇ *The child had to be raced to hospital.* **3** [T] (SPORT) to make an animal or a vehicle take part in a race

1 My sister is going to .... a race for charity.
2 The athlete who .... the race receives a gold medal.
3 Don't look behind you! You will .... the race.

9 Look at the example sentences in the dictionary entry. Then complete the sentences below with the correct preposition.

1 Jack came last .... the long-distance race.
2 It is a race .... time to save the Earth.

STUDY FOCUS | Collocations

Collocations are combinations of words which are often used together. When you learn a new word, use your dictionary to find collocations with that word. They are given in the example sentences of the entry.

10 Look at the dictionary entry for *football*. Find the collocations and complete the sentences.

> **football** 🔊 /ˈfʊtbɔːl/ *noun* (SPORT) **1** (*also* soccer) [U] a game that is played by two teams of eleven players who try to kick a round ball into a goal: *a football pitch/match* ❶ In the US **soccer** is the usual word for this game since Americans use the word **football** to refer to **American football**. **2** [C] the large round ball that is used in this game ➍ picture at **sport**

1 A football .... is a place where you play football.
2 A football .... usually lasts for 90 minutes.
3 In .... football, players can pick up the ball.

11 Look at the dictionary entry for *car*. Find the collocations in the example sentences of the entry and complete the sentences below.

> **car** 🔊 /kɑː(r)/ *noun* [C] **1** (*especially AmE* automobile) a road vehicle with four wheels that can carry a small number of people: *a new/second-hand car* ◇ *Where can I park the car?* ◇ *They had a car crash.* ◇ *to get into/out of a car* **2** (*BrE*) a section of a train that is used for a particular purpose: *a dining/sleeping car* **3** (*AmE*) =CARRIAGE (1)

1 There was a bad car .... this morning, but no one was injured.
2 I couldn't find anywhere to .... my car.
3 My father bought a .... car last week. It's four years old, but it looks like new.

STUDY FOCUS | Synonyms

Many words in English have a very similar meaning to other words. We call words that have similar meanings *synonyms*. In the *Oxford Student's Dictionary*, you can find a *Thesaurus* box which provides a list of synonyms and example sentences.

12 Look at the dictionary entry for *injure*. Choose the correct word to complete the sentences below, using the information in the *Thesaurus* box.

> **THESAURUS**
>
> injure
>
> wound · hurt · bruise · maim · sprain · pull · twist · strain
> These words all mean to harm yourself or sb else physically, especially in an accident.
> **injure**: *He was badly injured in a car crash.*
> **wound**: *Five people were seriously wounded in the attack.*
> **hurt**: *Did you hurt yourself?*
> **bruise**: *She had slipped and badly bruised her back.*
> **maim** (*formal*): *She was maimed in the accident.*
> **sprain**: *He fell and sprained his wrist/ankle/knee.*
> **pull**: *He pulled a muscle playing hockey.*
> **twist**: *She twisted her ankle/wrist/knee.*
> **strain**: *Using a computer can strain your eyes.*
>
> **injure** 🔊 🟩 /ˈɪndʒə(r)/ *verb* [T] to harm or hurt yourself or sb else physically, especially in an accident: *The goalkeeper seriously injured himself*

1 Adam worked all day at his computer and **strained / twisted** his eyes.
2 The soldier was seriously **wounded / bruised** in the attack.
3 Over 50 people were killed and over 100 people were **strained / injured**.
4 Our team captain **pulled / bruised** a muscle during the first half of the match.
5 The dancer **twisted / wounded** her ankle, but it wasn't **pulled / sprained**.

Irregular verb list

base form	past simple	past participle
be /biː/	was, were /wəz, wɒz, wə(r), wɜː(r)/	been /bɪn, biːn/
become /bɪ'kʌm/	became /bɪ'keɪm/	become /bɪ'kʌm/
begin /bɪ'gɪn/	began /bɪ'gæn/	begun /bɪ'gʌn/
bet /bet/	bet /bet/	bet /bet/
bite /baɪt/	bit /bɪt/	bitten /'bɪtn/
bleed /bliːd/	bled /bled/	bled /bled/
blow /bləʊ/	blew /bluː/	blown /bləʊn/
break /breɪk/	broke /brəʊk/	broken /'brəʊkən/
bring /brɪŋ/	brought /brɔːt/	brought /brɔːt/
build /bɪld/	built /bɪlt/	built /bɪlt/
burn /bɜːn/	burnt, burned /bɜːnt, bɜːnd/	burnt, burned /bɜːnt, bɜːnd/
buy /baɪ/	bought /bɔːt/	bought /bɔːt/
can /kən, kæn/	could /kəd, kʊd/	been able to /biːn 'eɪbl tə/
catch /kætʃ/	caught /kɔːt/	caught /kɔːt/
choose /tʃuːz/	chose /tʃəʊz/	chosen /'tʃəʊzn/
come /kʌm/	came /keɪm/	come /kʌm/
cost /kɒst/	cost /kɒst/	cost /kɒst/
cut /kʌt/	cut /kʌt/	cut /kʌt/
deal /diːl/	dealt /delt/	dealt /delt/
do /də, du/	did /dɪd/	done /dʌn/
draw /drɔː/	drew /druː/	drawn /drɔːn/
dream /driːm/	dreamt, dreamed /dremt, driːmd/	dreamt, dreamed /dremt, driːmd/
drive /draɪv/	drove /drəʊv/	driven /'drɪvn/
eat /iːt/	ate /eɪt, et/	eaten /'iːtn/
drink /drɪŋk/	drank /dræŋk/	drunk /drʌŋk/
fall /fɔːl/	fell /fel/	fallen /'fɔːlən/
feel /fiːl/	felt /felt/	felt /felt/
fight /faɪt/	fought /fɔːt/	fought /fɔːt/
find /faɪnd/	found /faʊnd/	found /faʊnd/
fly /flaɪ/	flew /fluː/	flown /fləʊn/
forget /fə'get/	forgot /fə'gɒt/	forgotten /fə'gɒtn/
forgive /fə'gɪv/	forgave /fə'geɪv/	forgiven /fə'gɪvn/
freeze /friːz/	froze /frəʊz/	frozen /'frəʊzn/
get /get/	got /gɒt/	got (AmE: gotten) /gɒt, 'gɒtn/
give /gɪv/	gave /geɪv/	given /'gɪvn/
go /gəʊ/	went /went/	gone, been /gɒn, biːn/
grow /grəʊ/	grew /gruː/	grown /grəʊn/
hang /hæŋ/	hung /hʌŋ/	hung /hʌŋ/
have /həv, hæv/	had /həd, hæd/	had /hæd/
hear /hɪə(r)/	heard /hɜːd/	heard /hɜːd/
hide /haɪd/	hid /hɪd/	hidden /'hɪdn/
hit /hɪt/	hit /hɪt/	hit /hɪt/
hold /həʊld/	held /held/	held /held/
hurt /hɜːt/	hurt /hɜːt/	hurt /hɜːt/
keep /kiːp/	kept /kept/	kept /kept/
know /nəʊ/	knew /njuː/	known /nəʊn/
lay /leɪ/	laid /leɪd/	laid /leɪd/
lead /liːd/	led /led/	led /led/
learn /lɜːn/	learnt, learned /lɜːnt, lɜːnd/	learnt, learned /lɜːnt, lɜːnd/
leave /liːv/	left /left/	left /left/

base form	past simple	past participle
lend /lend/	lent /lent/	lent /lent/
let /let/	let /let/	let /let/
light /laɪt/	lit /lɪt/	lit /lɪt/
lose /luːz/	lost /lɒst/	lost /lɒst/
make /meɪk/	made /meɪd/	made /meɪd/
mean /miːn/	meant /ment/	meant /ment/
meet /miːt/	met /met/	met /met/
pay /peɪ/	paid /peɪd/	paid /peɪd/
put /pʊt/	put /pʊt/	put /pʊt/
read /riːd/	read /red/	read /red/
ride /raɪd/	rode /rəʊd/	ridden /ˈrɪdn/
ring /rɪŋ/	rang /ræŋ/	rung /rʌŋ/
rise /raɪz/	rose /rəʊz/	risen /ˈrɪzn/
run /rʌn/	ran /ræn/	run /rʌn/
say /seɪ/	said /sed/	said /sed/
see /siː/	saw /sɔː/	seen /siːn/
sell /sel/	sold /səʊld/	sold /səʊld/
send /send/	sent /sent/	sent /sent/
set /set/	set /set/	set /set/
shake /ʃeɪk/	shook /ʃʊk/	shaken /ˈʃeɪkən/
shine /ʃaɪn/	shone /ʃɒn/	shone /ʃɒn/
shoot /ʃuːt/	shot /ʃɒt/	shot /ʃɒt/
show /ʃəʊ/	showed /ʃəʊd/	shown /ʃəʊn/
shut /ʃʌt/	shut /ʃʌt/	shut /ʃʌt/
sing /sɪŋ/	sang /sæŋ/	sung /sʌŋ/
sink /sɪŋk/	sank /sæŋk/	sunk /sʌŋk/
sit /sɪt/	sat /sæt/	sat /sæt/
sleep /sliːp/	slept /slept/	slept /slept/
smell /smel/	smelt, smelled /smelt, smeld/	smelt, smelled /smelt, smeld/
speak /spiːk/	spoke /spəʊk/	spoken /ˈspəʊkən/
spell /spel/	spelt, spelled /spelt, speld/	spelt, spelled /spelt, speld/
spend /spend/	spent /spent/	spent /spent/
spill /spɪl/	spilt, spilled /spɪlt, spɪld/	spilt, spilled /spɪlt, spɪld/
split /splɪt/	split /splɪt/	split /splɪt/
spoil /spɔɪl/	spoilt, spoiled /spɔɪlt, spɔɪld/	spoilt, spoiled /spɔɪlt, spɔɪld/
spread /spred/	spread /spred/	spread /spred/
stand /stænd/	stood /stʊd/	stood /stʊd/
steal /stiːl/	stole /stəʊl/	stolen /ˈstəʊlən/
stick /stɪk/	stuck /stʌk/	stuck /stʌk/
swim /swɪm/	swam /swæm/	swum /swʌm/
take /teɪk/	took /tʊk/	taken /ˈteɪkən/
teach /tiːtʃ/	taught /tɔːt/	taught /tɔːt/
tell /tel/	told /təʊld/	told /təʊld/
think /θɪŋk/	thought /θɔːt/	thought /θɔːt/
throw /θrəʊ/	threw /θruː/	thrown /θrəʊn/
understand /ˌʌndəˈstænd/	understood /ˌʌndəˈstʊd/	understood /ˌʌndəˈstʊd/
upset /ʌpˈset/	upset /ʌpˈset/	upset /ʌpˈset/
wake /weɪk/	woke /wəʊk/	woken /ˈwəʊkən/
wear /weə(r)/	wore /wɔː(r)/	worn /wɔːn/
win /wɪn/	won /wʌn/	won /wʌn/
write /raɪt/	wrote /rəʊt/	written /ˈrɪtn/

OXFORD
UNIVERSITY PRESS

Great Clarendon Street, Oxford, OX2 6DP, United Kingdom

Oxford University Press is a department of the University of Oxford.
It furthers the University's objective of excellence in research, scholarship,
and education by publishing worldwide. Oxford is a registered trade
mark of Oxford University Press in the UK and in certain other countries

© Oxford University Press 2014

The moral rights of the author have been asserted

First published in 2014

2018 2017 2016

10 9 8 7 6 5 4 3

No unauthorized photocopying

All rights reserved. No part of this publication may be reproduced, stored
in a retrieval system, or transmitted, in any form or by any means, without
the prior permission in writing of Oxford University Press, or as expressly
permitted by law, by licence or under terms agreed with the appropriate
reprographics rights organization. Enquiries concerning reproduction outside
the scope of the above should be sent to the ELT Rights Department, Oxford
University Press, at the address above

You must not circulate this work in any other form and you must impose
this same condition on any acquirer

Links to third party websites are provided by Oxford in good faith and for
information only. Oxford disclaims any responsibility for the materials
contained in any third party website referenced in this work

ISBN: 978 0 19 450602 1   Workbook
ISBN: 978 0 19 450607 6   Student Access Card
ISBN: 978 0 19 450606 9   Pack

Printed in China

This book is printed on paper from certified and well-managed sources

ACKNOWLEDGEMENTS

*The authors and publisher are grateful to those who have given permission to reproduce
the following extracts and adaptations of copyright material:* p.13 Extract from
Oxford Bookworm Library Stage 1: *The Adventures of Tom Sawyer* by Mark
Twain, retold by Nick Bullard. © Oxford University Press 2008. Reproduced by
permission.

p.29 Extract from Oxford Bookworm Library Stage 1: *Sherlock Holmes and the Sport
of Kings* by Sir Arthur Conan Doyle, retold by Jennifer Bassett. © Oxford
University Press 2008. Reproduced by permission.

p.45 Extract from Oxford Bookworm Library Stage 3: *Kidnapped* by Robert Louis
Stevenson, retold by Clare West. © Oxford University Press 2008. Reproduced
by permission.

p.61 Extract from Oxford Bookworm Library Stage 3: *The Railway Children* by Edith
Nesbit, retold by John Escott. © Oxford University Press 2008. Reproduced by
permission.

p.77 Extract from Oxford Bookworm Library Stage 4: *The Thirty-Nine Steps* by John
Buchan, retold by Nick Bullard. © Oxford University Press 2008. Reproduced
by permission.

pp.100-101 entries from the *Oxford Student's Dictionary*.

Cover: Patrick Boyer/Illustrations; Shutterstock (abstract blue background/
Toria), (teen boy working on laptop/holbox).
OUP Bookworms; "The Adventures of Tom Sawyer" Cover image by Stock-
byte/Punchstock
OUP Bookworms; "Sherlock Holmes and the Sport of Kings" Cover image by
Digital Vision/Punchstock
OUP Bookworms; "Kidnapped" Cover image by BBC
OUP Bookworms; "The Railway Children" Cover image by ITV Plc (Granada
International)/LFI/Randy Faris/Corbis
OUP Bookworms; "The Thirty-Nine Steps" Cover image by George F. Mobley/
National Geographic/Getty Images

Alamy Images pp6 (Montreal street/Ian Dagnall), 25 (Sinai Peninsula from
Space/Worldspec/NASA), 40 (black rucksack/Anton Starikov), 53 (underwater
cave/Carlos Villoch - MagicSea.com), 53 (teen girl with camera/Keith Levit),
66 (green eco background/TongRo Images), 70 (table tennis, Darius Knight/
Sport In Pictures), 76 (World Cup trophy/Associated Sports Photography), 76
(teen girl playing tennis/Daniel Dempster Photography), 78 (Alton Towers
Oblivion ride/Andrew Fox), 80 (frog on fork/Stockex), 81 (running water/BSIP
SA); Getty Images pp7 (portrait Hispanic boy/Juanmonino), 17 (portrait teen
girl/Neustockimages), 21 (portrait businesswoman in street/Paul Bradbury),
21 (teen boy on bike/Bill Reitzel), 21 (teen girl portrait/Brand X Pictures), 22
(group of mountain hikers/Antonio D'Albore), (portrait of girl outdoors/Hero
images), 38 (Clark's nutcracker/James Hager/Robert Harding World Imagery),
40 (Sir Isaac Newton/English School/The Bridgeman Art Library), 42 (Florence
Nightingale/Underwood Archives), 44 (teen boy reading/Alys Tomlinson),
44 (women in shopping centre, Kuwait/Celia Peterson), 47 (cycling race/
Pablo Blazquez Dominguez), 51 (two people skiing in Alps/JACQUES Pierre /

hemis.fr), 53 (boy kayaking/Inti St Clair), 53 (teen boy portrait/Terry Vine), 54
(school boy/Plush Studios), 54 (student using computer in class/Thomas Bar-
wick), 59 (Susie Wolff/Ker Robertson), 59 (Nuri Sahin/Bongarts), 62 (Songdo
at night/Sungjin Kim), 73 (Daniel Ricciardo lifting trophy/Mathias Kniepeiss),
73 (Ireland rugby players/AFP), 73 (playing tennis/Design Pics/Stock Foundry),
73 (Pyrenees ski resort/Anger O.), 73 (four cyclists/Image Source), 73 (athletes
running race/Clerkenwell), 73 (Kobe Bryant/AFP), 76 (woman skiing/Bogdan
Angheloiu), 79 (smiling boy outdoors/Maskot), 81 (Chiang Mai Province,
Thailand/Design Pics/Keith Levit), 83 (Tewkesbury flooding/Matt Cardy); Mas-
terfile p57 (tour guide); OUP pp3 (Chinese teen boy/Mark Bassett), 4 (teen girl
portrait/Chris King), 8 (girl with braces/David Jordan) 10 (two boys in cafe/
Mark Bassett), 21 (middle-aged man/Gareth Boden), 27 (diver with camera/
SIani), 30 (food pie chart/ifong), 30 (hiker/Laurence Mouton), 30 (girl with
plait/Mark Bassett), 30 (portrait of man/Radius Images), 32 (steamed white
rice/Elena Elisseeva), 32 (French fries/D. Hurst), 32 (hamburger/Ingram), 32
(chocolate pieces/Craig Holmes), 32 (bowl of porridge/Keith Leighton), 32
(assorted biscuits/latham & holmes), 32 (apples/David Cook), 32 (whole fish/
Stockbyte), 33 (eating salad/White), 36 (blueberry muffin/Lew Robertson), 36
(cheeseburger/Photodisc), 48 (mountain biking/Al Churcher), 51 (sailing boat/
Jack Sullivan), 53 (bungee jumping/Ammit Jack), 57 (nurse making bed/Digi-
tal Vision), 57 (car mechanic/Valueline), 73 (football stadium/Eduard SolÀ),
81 (cut finger/Image Source); Press Association Images pp38 (chimp doing
memory test/Tetsuro Matsuzawa/AP), 46 (Ewan McGregor and Charley Boor-
man/Jean/EMPICS Entertainment); Rex Features pp31 (Usain Bolt Olympics/
Top Photo Group), 47 (Stunt Motorcyclist Chris Bromham/Malcolm Clarke/
Associated Newspapers), 48 (astronaut exiting capsule/KeystoneUSA-ZUMA),
57 (architect drawing/Jim Pickerell), 74 (Rafael Nadal/Bebert Bruno/SIPA);
Shutterstock pp7 (Msida Parish Church, Valletta, Malta/FooTToo), 11 (Big Ben/
Luciano Mortula), 14 (Asain teen girl/Jack Z Young), 14 (Shanghai skyline pan-
orama/chungking), 18 (aeroplane taking off/Andrew Barker), 19 (smiling teen
student/michaeljung), 24 (Bridge of Sighs, Oxford/PHB.cz (Richard Semik)),
24 (student using laptop in cafe/Dean Drobot), 24 (woman hiking/vladis.
studio), 27 (tropical beach/Elena Rudakova), 40 (old dirty trainers/phomphan),
42 (doctor's stethoscope/Tish1), 43 (Shakespeare's Globe, London/Ron Ellis),
53 (group rafting/Maxim Petrichuk), 57 (lawyer with law code/Kzenon), 57
(librarian sorting books/ChameleonsEye), 57 (man doing accounts/Robert Kn-
eschke), 57 (man using computer and laptops/Andrey_Popov), 57 (electrician
fixing fuse box/Dmitry Kalinovsky), 57 (fashion designer drawing/Slaven),
65 (Yorkshire countryside/Andrew Roland), 73 (high school basketball court/
spirit of america), 76 (umbrella in rain/Brian A Jackson), 81 (runner with injured ankle/Warren Goldswain), 81 (bruised arm/lzf), 81 (broken thigh x-ray/
Praisaeng), 81 (grazed skin/schankz).

Illustrations by: Andy Parker pp63; Chris Koelle/Portland Studios pp 45 (OUP
Bookworms/Kidnapped); Javier Joaquin/The Organisation pp9, 55; Jon Mitch-
ell/Beehive pp69; Laura Martinez/Sylvie Poggio pp 39, 41; Paul Daviz pp 5,15,
23, 65; Paul Fisher-Johnson pp13 (OUP Bookworms/The Adventures of Tom
Sawyer); Ron Tiner pp29 (OUP Bookworms/Sherlock Holmes and the Sport of
Kings; Simon Rumble/Beehive pp4, 17, 49, 58, 79